FINDING GOD IN SCIENCE

The Extraordinary Evidence For
The Soul And Christianity,
A Rocket Scientist's Gripping Odyssey

MICHAEL O'CONNELL

Eigen Publishing

Revised Print Edition V1.7

FINDING GOD IN SCIENCE

The Extraordinary Evidence For The Soul And Christianity, A Rocket Scientist's Gripping Odyssey

By Michael O'Connell

Revised Print Edition © 2023, Version 1.7

First Published © 2016 ISBN 978-0-9973690-3-8

Michael O'Connell
Eigen Publishing
Orange County, California

Cover Image: a composite image of galaxy Messier 82 revealed in X-rays, infrared light and hydrogen emissions. Courtesy: NASA, ESA, CXC, and JPL-Caltech, Hubble.

To God's glory and to my wonderful family.

CONTENTS

Contents Continued ...

Contents Continued ...

Contents Continued ...

Contents Continued ...

The views and opinions in this work are strictly those of the author, and are not the views of the National Aeronautics and Space Administration, the Jet Propulsion Laboratory, or the California Institute of Technology.

ACKNOWLEDGEMENTS

I want to acknowledge my wonderful wife who encouraged me to see this project through despite the seemingly endless hours of writing and rewriting, and for her insightful comments. Thanks as well to my daughters and their husbands for their interest and encouragement, and to Greg Campbell and Robert Bagby, who coached me through some of the project's rocky times. Thanks to Dr. William Havlicek for his insightful advice and to David Glen for his editing and beautiful layout.

I also want to give a special thanks to those who gave me invaluable feedback on the project: Michael Christian, Carol Henderson, Dr. William Blair, Dr. C. Robert O'Dell, Patrick O'Connell, Kristin Birch, David Birch, Marian Lee Hilker, Beth Randolph, Bob Mandrioli, Chaz Blackledge, Greg Gabrenya and Dr. Randy Isaac.

~ Michael O'Connell

AUTHOR'S PREFACE

WHY FINDING GOD?

"When the Spirit of truth comes, He will guide you into all the truth, for He will not speak on His own authority, but whatever He hears He will speak, and He will declare to you the things that are to come."
~ John 16:13, English Standard Version

Friends call me a rocket scientist. I was an engineer at the Jet Propulsion Laboratory, which is nestled in the foothills of the rugged and verdant San Gabriel Mountains in Southern California. It is America's premier NASA space science and technology center, operated by the California Institute of Technology. I worked in the highly analytical world of space science engineering, and I have been a Christian and a student of the Bible from childhood. This is my chronicle of discovery, the peaks and valleys of my career, the triumphs and losses in the enterprise of space, and of my Christian faith.

This work began with my own personal struggle between atheistic claims based in science, and my Christian faith. *Finding God in Science* reveals the consistency of scripture and science in an accessible way, and without adding anything to scripture. It reasserts Christianity in a postmodern culture. *Finding God in Science* is the first book to demonstrate that Christ's earthly message and mission follow the natural laws of the universe, revealing a Divine premeditation. The science in *Finding God* demonstrates the nature of truth, what it means to know God, and communicate with Him. *Finding God in Science* sheds new light on the mystery of why Christ had to die to save us from our sins, and why we have to die to finally realize eternal life. It illustrates how Jesus Christ could be both God and man, and it describes the indwelling of the Holy Spirit. It also backs the security of our salvation.

As incredible as it may sound, these claims are based on new inferences from quantum physics, which has a deep and unexpected relevance to Christianity. I believe insights implied by deep physical reality have the power to reframe the modern defense of God and the Christian faith.

At Purdue University, I had no idea that my engineering degree would eventually take me to California to work on the B-1 bomber, and then to space science engineering. For forty two years, I had the privilege of working in flight testing of the B-1, preflight testing for the Delta II rocket, and vibration testing for numerous space science missions. These ranged from the Wide Field Planetary Cameras, used in the Hubble Space Telescope, to a long line of spacecraft including the Mars Reconnaissance Orbiter; Kepler the planet finder; Planck, the background radiation observatory, the Orbiting Carbon Observatory 2, and the newest Mars surface rover Curiosity.

The engineering specialty of vibration ensures that science equipment and spacecraft can withstand the heavy structural vibrations induced by a rocket launch. Vibration can cause sensitive science equipment to fail. My professional career has given me firsthand experience analyzing vibration wave phenomena. These bear striking similarities to other waves in physics, like those described by quantum mechanics.

My conversion to Christianity came about through the simple question of a young friend, when I was about ten years old. He said, "Do you believe in Jesus?" We were in Sunday school and I looked at the picture of Jesus on the wall in front of us. As I turned, I noticed a Sunday school teacher sitting behind me. I didn't want to say no, so I said, "I don't know." My friend Rick Willmann just smiled warmly and said, "I do."

No one had ever asked me this before and it took me aback. For the first time, I became aware of a profound emptiness in my soul. Somehow this brief experience spurred me to find out if God was real, if that was possible.

I decided to run an experiment. I did not speak to anyone about this, but I decided to pray for rain and see if it occurred. Though I prayed several times for rain nothing happened. I was disappointed, but a couple of weeks later at church, I read a story about a young man who humbly accepted responsibility for his ball going into his neighbor's yard. This pleased both God and his neighbor. This, and other Bible stories I had heard, gave me the idea to pray in humility and faith, rather than to simply test God.

I waited for a cloudless sunny day, and that evening I prayed for rain for the farmers and the flowers, and to help other people. I also prayed saying that I knew that God could do this, but that He was not bound to make it rain, and that His will be done. To my astonishment it rained hard the very next day, and I was extremely happy!

But within a couple of days doubts crept in. I wondered if the whole thing had been a coincidence, and if I was fooling myself. I decided to pray for rain a second time, in the same attitude of trust. I waited for another completely clear day and prayed again. It rained hard again the very next day, and I was elated. I felt as light as sunshine. I was so happy to know that God is real, and that He cared enough to reach out to me.

You may think this sounds rather childish. Yet this was just the beginning of a long line of answered prayers, God experiences, and rational thinking that continue to convince me that God is real, and that He cares for me.

I kept my faith into adulthood, but I retained some childish ideas about the creation passages of the Bible. Even as a young engineer, I was a strict "creationist" of sorts and completely against any consideration of evolution. Still, I recognized that proponents of creation science were consistently off base in their musings.

In the 1980's, through the Jet Propulsion Laboratory's (JPL) missions to the planets, I came to believe that stars and planetary systems really do evolve, even at the present time. About the same time, I began to recognize the broad range of evidence for biological evolution, particularly through programs like Carl Sagan's *Cosmos*. As a young believer, I found his arguments for evolution to be powerful and deeply disturbing.

As a result, I entered one of those long desert periods that people of faith sometimes go through. How was I to get beyond the atheist's challenges to my faith? I wanted to discover once and for all if the Bible could be reconciled with science. To make matters worse, I did not know anyone in the Church to help me sort out the issues. My Christian mentors were not familiar with science, nor did they put much stock in it. I felt completely alone in the matter, except for God's presence, and I was chagrined to suddenly find myself at the periphery of the circle of faith.

So began my odyssey to find out how literally God's message in the Bible could be taken, and if science and Genesis could be reconciled. I wondered if science could substantiate any of Christ's claims, though this seemed a vain hope at the time. I embarked on the journey of which Saint Paul wrote, "When I became a man, I gave up childish ways."[1] So it was with science and Christianity for a young engineer from Indiana.

Sadly, my predicament was not unique. Millions of people struggle, in lonely isolation, with doubts and apprehensions over atheistic claims about God and science. Colleges and intellectuals are turning many people away from the Christian faith, but it is possible to answer their charges in a convincing way. God has real answers that are reasonable, beautiful and consistent with science, yet jarringly unconventional. It is possible to find God even in science. It is certainly possible for the Church to blunt its marginalization with right thinking about truth and science, thereby removing a stumbling block to the gospel.

Finding God has given me more confidence in Christianity, and it provides a new language to tell the gospel—one that has a direct correspondence with known physical principles. The resolution of faith and science that I found was not quick or easy, and reinforcement of my Christian faith did not come through science alone. Christian friendships, the Gospel of John, and the film of the same name, were all instrumental in bolstering my faith in Christ.

Bible prophecies fulfilled by Jesus Christ are especially convincing for me. These were written by numerous authors, centuries before Christ and their fulfillment makes them unique in all literature. Here are but a few highlights. Isaiah 7:14 declares that Christ would be born of a virgin, and that He would be called 'God With Us.' Isaiah 53 is a detailed prophecy of the Christ who suffers for our iniquities. Psalm 22 describes the Messiah's suffering on the cross in vivid detail, saying, "They pierced My hands and My feet." Daniel 9:24-27 gives a timeline for the appearance of Jesus Christ, and it says, "Messiah shall be cut off, but not for Himself."

Christianity certainly has plenty of good arguments in its favor, the most compelling of which are often based on personal experience. This is why the personal conduct of Christians is so important. But, given the prevalence of postmodern thought, these arguments and experiences are less accessible to people nowadays.

Of course, no one may know the entire method, depth, or breadth of God's action in the world. We try to put the things of God into words, but ultimately they are beyond human comprehension. We do not even have a complete model of physics. Furthermore, resolving faith and science does not bring salvation in itself. Nor does it revise the gospel of Jesus Christ, or add to scripture. Neither does knowledge supplant the primacy of love, but love without knowledge leads to folly. The sharing of the love of God requires true knowledge. Therefore, learning should be an act of worship, and defending the faith an act of love.

Believers accept Christ because the Holy Spirit bears witness to the truth in our spirits. But the study of God's hand in nature, through the grand narrative of science has the power to reconnect our faith to the physical world, heighten our awareness of God, and persuade the doubting heart. So, I write in the spirit of Erwin Schrödinger who observed, "Some of us should venture to embark on a synthesis of facts and theories, albeit with second-hand and incomplete knowledge of some of them—and at the risk of making fools of ourselves."[2] I make myself a fool now for Christ.

You do not have to be a scientist to engage and understand the philosophical implications of the science in *Finding God*. Former atheist Antony Flew champions the non-scientist who ponders the Divine implications of science: "When you ask how it is that those subatomic particles—or anything physical— could exist and why, you are engaged in philosophy. When you draw philosophical conclusions from scientific data, then you are thinking as a philosopher."[3] Stephen Hawking also believes that the most complicated science is, "understandable in broad principle by everyone, not just a few scientists."[4] So in this matter we are all more or less on equal footing.

In a way, scientific theories and equations are metaphors, mere symbols on paper. But they are special metaphors that correspond to the way things really are, in some deep way. It is true that we as human beings are still struggling to understand some very basic things about the universe, but this does not diminish what mankind has already learned, which is considerable.

Carl Sagan used to say "extraordinary claims require extraordinary evidence", and extraordinary evidence is what I aim to present in favor of God, the human soul and Christianity. I offer unexpected perceptions from nature that buttress the Christian faith, in the spirit of Christ's own nature-based teachings. You may find the most sensational evidence for God to be incredible, but every word is true.

CHAPTER ONE

WHY SHOULD I CARE ABOUT SCIENCE?

"If, therefore, the whole church comes together and all speak... fallaciously about science... and outsiders or unbelievers enter, will they not say that you are out of your minds?" Rephrase of 1 Corinthians 14:23, English Standard Version

Modern science points like a beacon toward the Creator of the universe, like an indelible proof mark of God on nature. Deep space science, biology and particle physics reveal, to an increasing degree, the handiwork of a vast Intelligence. Yet as a people we believe less now than before.

England, for instance, was an anchor of Christian devotion and doctrinal reform—a center of great spiritual revivals—until the last century. In the last generation Church attendance there has fallen to less than 10 percent of the population, and Church attendance in most of Europe is equally languid.

In fact, the West is being conquered by a false religion, and Christianity, the West's benefactor, is in retreat now in America as it is in Europe. But, unlike the false religions of Biblical times, an atheistic secularism is the rising modern religion. This modern atheism, that claims science as its basis, is one of the greatest and most complex challenges the Church has ever faced. Postmodern views that totally reject truth have also emerged from atheism. These views are an existential threat to the very fabric of our society.

Theologian Alistair McGrath warns, "We live in an era when apologetics has ceased to be peripheral to the task of the church... Christians want to be equipped to deal with their friends' hard questions, but they also need to be reassured about their own anxieties, fears, and misgivings, which are often marginalized or ignored by doubtless well-meaning preachers."[1]

It is clear then, that a reasoned defense of the faith that is consistent with science, is desperately needed.

TECHNOLOGY AND A YOUNG ENGINEER

You may be asking yourself if science and space exploration are really worth our time and treasure. But, the successes of science and modern technology have made theories and arguments based in science extraordinarily compelling. Indeed, science and aerospace technology molded the entirety of my education and career, as it has for countless others.

As a kid I always wanted to work on airplanes, and I dreamed of owning my own aircraft company. In 1969 the local paper published a graduation picture of me and my senior high school bandmates. It was a poignant photograph. I think that all of us realized that our lives would change forever upon graduation. We sensed that few of us would be staying near our families and friends, or the small town in which we had spent our entire lives. I knew my dreams of aviation engineering would take me far from home.

At Purdue I interviewed with McDonnell Douglas, not once, but three times, over the course of two years. It appeared that a job awaited me at the fighter aircraft manufacturer upon graduation. But when the time came, the F-15 budget had been cut back and a hiring freeze was in effect. I was frozen out of my dream job.

At the same time, I interviewed with a representative from Rockwell International who told me straight out, "You will be getting a job offer, but probably not from the electric boat division or the B-1 bomber division, since they are both laying off people." A few weeks later I received a letter from the B-1 division offering me a job with a beginning salary that seemed huge to a young man from rural Indiana. I was going to work on an aircraft after all! The catch? I had to move across the country to El Segundo, a west coast beach town near Los Angeles, California.

Dad encouraged me saying, "Look at moving to California as an adventure, and return home in five years if it doesn't work out." I figured I would be back long before that if things didn't go well. My dad reassured me saying, "Remember that any bad situation can be changed." So, move to California it was. I flew alone to Los Angeles in June of 1973, on a TWA Boeing 707, carrying only two modest suitcases and a duffle bag.

It was not easy to be so far from home, but I found that a positive 'can do' attitude pervaded my circle in California. There was an aura of daring and optimism. I went west not knowing just how much there would be to see and do, or how much I would like the climate, and the women. I would eventually marry one of them from Hollywood, a girl with midwestern roots. But to that end I found that to have friends, I had to become more friendly, open up a little and be more daring myself. I had to become more like my father the storyteller, and a little less like my genial, but very private mother.

My father, his brothers and my grandfather were all great storytellers. They repeated many of their stories again, and again. Their tales were so entertaining none of us minded hearing again how my dad beat up some obnoxious bully that was picking on another poor soul. We loved hearing about the Tom Sawyer existence that my uncle Pat and his friends enjoyed during his high school days, with a secret cabin, hunting and weekends in the woods.

My dad's family hunted to put food on the table, and we savored the story of Granddad letting a rabbit escape alive during a hunt. The rabbit had just survived a fusillade from half a dozen fellow hunters, and one of his four sons took a second aim at the frightened animal. Granddad exclaimed, "You kill that rabbit, and I'll knock you into the middle of next week!" The rabbit lived to see another day.

Working on the indomitable B-1 bomber in California was a move in the right direction. The B-1 is a sleek four engine, low altitude supersonic bomber that can carry more weaponry than a B-52, and it is a good deal faster, with better avionics. The B-1 lineage includes the world beating North American Aviation P-51 and F-86 fighter planes, the F-100 Super Sabre, and the X-15 rocket plane. Only the company name changed when Rockwell acquired North American Aviation.

I was finally able to buy a car that I had wanted for so long. Mother was very frugal, and made our family's money go a long way. I followed this financial pattern when I ordered my first car– a 1973 Camaro– a sensible plain version with a 6 cylinder engine. But, not many Camaros were sold with 6 cylinder engines in California back then. The only car available in my color was a sleek upgraded model with a V-8 engine. I felt guilty spending more for a flashier car, but driving it quickly cured me of my misgivings. I kept that car for 18 years. From this I learned that spending more on a better product can be less expensive, in the long run, than being overly frugal.

Even so, junior engineering was not as exciting as I imagined. My first day on the job, my supervisor Jerry Sullivan took me aside and said, "You may find some of the guys are a bit down in the mouth, because we are laying people off. But you should be okay for at least a year since the government pays us to take on new grads." Such was my introduction to the world of aerospace, but I liked Mr. Sullivan. He was a good supervisor and a fair man, though I did not work for him very long.

My job was to prepare drawing corrections for the B-1 crew module structure. Disappointingly, the airframe design was already complete, and only minor corrections were being made to drawings, as assembly problems arose. I received little guidance from my lead man, who was too busy to shepherd me. I did learn how to verify the intent of proposed design changes, but my situation was a let down. Some engineers had been laid off after the B-70 cancellation and hired back at a lower salary. Discouragement and uncertainty hung in the air. To be fair, Mr. Sullivan had warned me on my first day at work.

Then for a time it seemed I would be transferred to Palmdale, in the high desert, where the bomber was being assembled. Moving to LA took some getting used to, but relocating to the desert was more than I could do. It felt like being consigned to Siberia. I began brooding, and I let my boss know that I did not want to go. To my relief I was able to stay in El Segundo, but I was soon transferred to the wing stress group.

For the next several months, day after day, I made repetitive calculations of areas and moments of inertia by hand. The data was for a stress model of the B-1 wing, which had to be entered into a deck of punch cards that would be fed into a main- frame IBM computer. Wing stresses were computed and reviewed by another more senior engineer. If the run 'bombed', or didn't work, we had to figure out which computer cards contained the errors, correct them and resubmit the job. It was tedious work, and since the wing was already designed, there did not seem to be much hope of advancing within the ranks. I began referring to this as the 'stress clerk' phase of my career.

One day my supervisor Mr. Riley sternly called me into his office. My jocular friend Eric Hodges called him Smiley Riley, because he never smiled. Mr. Riley remarked on my lack of enthusiasm for clerical stress work, and that he was loaning me to Atomics International for several weeks, along with a few other guys. I was to work temporarily at another Rockwell division in Canoga Park, which made for a long drive to work in the world famous Los Angeles traffic.

My new supervisor Paul Savage was an enthusiastic boss and he took me under his wing right away. I got to do some real engineering for a change, actual stress calculations for a heavy lift fixture. It would be used to lift a nuclear reactor steam generator. Most interesting of all, I developed a preliminary design for an underwater pressure vessel and presented my findings to a review board. All this work was done with pencil and paper, a slide rule, handbooks, and a desktop calculator.

My time at Atomics International passed all too quickly, and I began to dread my return to the clerical stress world under Mr. Riley. To my surprise, bright and early on my first day back at the B-1 Division, Smiley Riley called me into his office and announced, "I am transferring you to the B-1 dynamics group. You'll be analyzing vibration and acoustic flight data on the bomber." Real flight data!

I could hardly believe my luck as I met my new group supervisor Al Englebreckt. He was for me a sort of gregarious father figure and our personalities clicked immediately. My new lead man Al Tipton was more skeptical of me at first, but I knew I had found a new work home. God had delivered me from the disappointments of my bumpy career start. One of my new associates, Dennis Kern, would later take me into the vibration group at the Jet Propulsion Laboratory (JPL).

At about this same time, the Lord provided California parents for me in Don and Betty Munger. This fine Christian couple gave me room and board for the next three years, and I soaked up their care and selfless love like a sponge. They provided stability to my lonely life when my own family was so far away, in Indiana.

At one point during my B-1 adventure, it fell to me to observe the vibration on the weapon's bay doors, to make sure they would not tear off when opened at high speed and low altitude. Twice I went to Edwards Air Force Base to watch strip charts of door vibration data, in real time. It was a genuine treat, but it was also terrifying. It was my job to warn the test team and bomber crew if the vibration became excessive. Such a condition could even result in the loss of the bomber.

This was terrifying because I was not really sure how to recognize danger in the strip chart data. How big did the vibration peaks really have to be to pose a threat? Roger Tyler, the man I replaced for the day, was encouraging, but not very helpful. He had no example vibration data to show me, due to security restrictions. He simply said, "You will know it when you see it. You'll do fine!" I was relieved when the weapon's bay portion of each flight test was successfully completed, and I was able to make the long drive back home, mission accomplished.

Once leaving the air base in my Camaro, I saw the B-1 and its chase plane flying their flight test circuit, and both aircraft were coming across the road ahead of me. I stepped on the gas to close the distance, and watched the B-1 and its F-111 chase plane fly at nearly Mach 1 across the road ahead. The roar of the massive jet engines zoomed past my car's nose. Talk about exciting! I only wish that I had gotten a photograph.

The delivery of nuclear weapons was, of course, crucial to the mission design of the B-1, and this was a sobering fact. For a short while I wondered if I really wanted to work on a nuclear bomber. A single B-1 could incinerate more people than I can imagine. Consulting the Bible, I took the matter to thoughtful prayer. I realized that, believing in a strong defense of our way of life, indeed of the Christianized world, I should be willing to help build such weapons. In this way I made peace with the B-1.

My last job on the B-1 was working to reduce the crew cabin noise. I was sent to Edwards Air Force Base to take crew cabin noise measurements inside the bomber, while it was hooked up to a ground cooling power cart. Amazingly, I was the only person inside the bomber for the duration of the noise test. I sat in the pilot seat and moved about the cabin, collecting noise measurements for about an hour and completed my notes.

I drove off the Edwards Base and headed for home, thankful to have been inside such an amazing machine, even for a short time. Later, I performed a noise test of several different air conditioning vent designs in an acoustic chamber, with pressurized air passing through each type of vent. It was a challenging problem, but I left Rockwell for JPL before the cabin noise job was completed.

It was about this time that I first became acquainted with the work of the creation scientists. As interesting as their arguments were, I could see problems with many of their assumptions, and that they were misinterpreting many basic points of science. Creation science was tantalizing, but it did not provide satisfactory answers.

By 1976, I started attending Lake Avenue Church in Pasadena. It had a terrific Sunday school class for unmarried college graduates, with 300 members. I began to develop fast friendships with a clique of young men and women. I had never been a part of such a close group of friends before, and I was soon dating several girls. It was there that I met the love of my life, Myra Lynn Myers.

One night in late December, our church group had a Christmas dinner party. At the time I had a crush on another woman named Janice, and my hope was to get to know her better at the party. But when I arrived I found myself standing behind a very attractive woman. I decided that I had to meet her. To my surprise, when she turned around it was Myra, who I already knew. I said, “Its you!” And we both laughed out loud.

That evening the blinders came off. I began to realize how attractive Myra was, and how much fun she was compared to the woman I had been chasing for months. I realized that Janice simply did not like me the same way Myra did. She was sensual, funny and had a way of diffusing conflict with a disarming playfulness and humor. My feelings for Myra soon became serious. She won my heart with laughter, her love of God and life, and her love for me.

A year later we were married, and twenty two months after that our first baby came along. By the end of our first five years together we had three daughters. Finally, I felt like a complete person, a real man raising a family. Eventually we settled in a white Cape Cod style home near JPL, with a view of the San

Gabriel mountains. It seemed an idyllic setting in which to raise our family, and God seemed to work things out for us whatever the obstacles.

By 1980 the B-1 division was struggling to survive off what had become a protracted flight test program. It was clear that if the country's politics did not change soon, the entire division's assets would be sold off, and the organization would close its doors. The long term outlook for my job was bleak. The B-1 was eventually produced years later, but I did not want to wait around to see what would become of me.

When the chance came I jumped ship, and went to work at JPL for one of my old work mates, Dennis Kern. Before JPL, the closest I had gotten to rocketry was lighting off bottle rockets in my dad's back acreage. The tiny missiles were supplied by our cousins from Florida. It was energizing to be a part of the high tech world of space exploration, and it was no small thing to have a stable engineering job near my church and friends.

My first job at JPL was cataloging system structural drawings and vibration data from previous JPL spacecraft tests. It was not flashy work, but it familiarized me with JPL's heritage, and the types of spacecraft they had flown. When the Space Shuttle started its test flight program in 1981, I was given the job of evaluating its acoustic noise and vibration data. I was excited to be doing what I had done with B-1 flight test data on the Space Shuttle!

I wrote several reports documenting Shuttle flight data results, and was published for the first time. I generated acoustic predictions for the Wide Field/Planetary Camera (WFPC) and the Hubble Space Telescope, that would be put into orbit within the Space Shuttle's fourteen foot wide cargo bay. My objective was to determine the vibration and acoustic test environments that would prove JPL's camera system could survive the tremendous rigors of a rocket launch.

It was during this period that doubts began creeping into my thinking about God, because of the atheistic claims made by the likes of Carl Sagan. I could feel the weight of atheism pressing in on me. I was aware of creation science, but I found their speculative ideas more akin to political opinion than scientific data and theories. I knew that God was still with me, but I didn't know anyone who could help me work through the science based questions and ideas that were plaguing me. I took the matter to God and waited.

THE NEW SECULARISM

Now secularism is not bad, per se. The American form of government is essentially secular, and it was so devised by a deeply Christian people, in order to keep the government and Church from corrupting each other. But atheistic secularism goes far beyond the simple constitutional prohibition of a state church. Its aim is the elimination of religion from all public discourse and policy by marginalizing Christianity, in the hope that religion will eventually disappear on its own.

Atheists insist that God is simply an explanation of mysteries and puzzling physical phenomena. Now that science has shown us the truth about how things work, there is no more need for God, or so they say.

Secularists use the appearance of scientific knowledge to promote an anti-God worldview, which is a form of slander—using science to discredit the Creator. They assume Him away, as Lee Smolin does in *Three Roads to Quantum Gravity*, "So the first principle of cosmology must be, "There is nothing outside the universe.""[2] Then, when God does not show up in experimentation, the circular logic concludes that God does not exist. But knowing how nature works does not eliminate God. He is not part of the universe.

It is no coincidence that religious affiliation started its current decline, particularly in Europe, shortly after Charles Darwin published the Origin of Species. Sure enough, other important things were taking place at the same time. The industrial age began to move into high gear, and Americans and Europeans were busy federalizing themselves into modern secular governments. In the twentieth century, two world wars took a terrible toll on the psyche and well being of the West, especially in Europe. Then, post war prosperity brought a sense of self sufficiency and materialism. Through out these events, there was a growing acceptance of atheistic beliefs rooted in science, which are in direct opposition to Christian doctrine.

The public is taught, and is coming to believe, that the Bible contains myths that no longer have the power to lay claim to one's behavior. The posture of nearly every Western government run school system is multicultural ambivalence, even hostility, toward the very moral and religious principles that formed Western societies. Many of those that stay in the Christian faith are frightfully ignorant of the Bible. Others think the Bible can be changed to suit current ideas, even accepting beliefs that actually undermine Christianity.

AN UNPRECEDENTED CLASH OF IDEAS

Like it or not, Christian believers are embroiled in a titanic intellectual clash quite unlike anything the Church has faced. It is a kind of ideological guerrilla war, for the soul of Western culture. The debate rages even in countries entirely dominated by atheistic propaganda, as in the former Soviet Union. Nikita Khrushchev, once the Soviet Premier, felt compelled to make the fatuous observation that, "Gagarin flew into space, but didn't see any God there."[3]

Christians should not have any illusions about the irreconcilable gulf between atheistic secularism, and the Christian faith. The leftists, that are driving the national agenda toward an authoritarian system, know that Christianity must be co-opted, or silenced if their agenda is to succeed.

Christians are increasingly marginalized for being guided by "superstition," and for being narrow and non inclusive, even though Christianity is for the salvation of all people. Ironically, the justification for this is that Christians are said to "discriminate", even though we only seek to follow God in moral behavior. Unfortunately, the debate about God has come to a retractable momentum, and atheists have gained the upper hand on the contemporary public stage.

Many pastors think they should avoid social issues and only preach the gospel. By this the Church has been complicit in its own marginalization, by its silence in the face of increasing evil. How can the Church be salt and light if it does not speak about cultural matters of morality, which are the purview of the Church? Jesus approached people with grace, but also with truth. Because of this He said, "(the world) hates Me because I testify of it that its works are evil."[4]

Theologically, an all powerful Creator must necessarily embody truth. By extension, His truth should be found in nature. If it proves anything at all, science and technology demonstrate that a privileged truth does exist in nature, corroborating this tenet. The postmodern view that there is "no real truth" is as much the enemy of science, as it is of Christianity. Many postmodern people view scientific theories as mere "social constructs". But science is not simply an alternate view of reality. Science reveals, as well as human beings can quantify, physical truth, and physical truth mirrors the truth that is God.

In our day, the strength of evidence that Christians present for God's existence, and for our faith, will determine the future vitality of the Church. Our action, or lack of it, will determine whether society will continue to move away from its Christian roots. If we do not meet this challenge, I fear that Christianity and liberty are destined to become minor features of Western society.[5]

AN UNNECESSARY SEPARATION

Historically, science is a form of wisdom that has not been foreign to the Church. Indeed, many of the most prominent scientists have been believers, including the likes of Francis Bacon (the scientific method), Copernicus (solar system mechanics), Galileo (planets and planetary motion), Kepler (laws of planetary motion), Isaac Newton (law of gravitation and mechanics), Faraday (electromagnetics), Fleming (inventor of the diode), Lister (antiseptic surgery), James Maxwell (electromagnetic theory of light), Samuel Morse (the telegraph), and Francis Collins (decoding the human DNA genome).[6] Of course, many others could be added to the list.

Science generally takes the most reasonable interpretation of physical facts, and not simply the most adversarial view to religion. Certainly, if one professor is free to say God has nothing to do with creation or life, then another should be free to say there is a Creator. But science is self-correcting, and every young scientist dreams of discovering something new that will upend the "apple cart", and rewrite science books. Francis Collins observes wryly, "That's what Nobel Prizes are given for."[7] Presently, scientists are not a unified mass that can be marshaled by anti-religious zealots.

The Big Lie is that the secular worldview is the only logical conclusion from the physical facts of science. Many Christians have bought into this atheistic conclusion, which is why so many believers have chosen to disbelieve whole fields of science, like cosmology and evolution. Many other Christians have been left to grapple with issues of faith and science on their own, being pulled between actual science, and scientific-sounding opinions, essentially based on a particular interpretation of Genesis.

Unfortunately, many leaders in the Church have cut themselves off from what they regard as secular scientific knowledge. I have known many devout and intelligent Christians who think scientific theories are bunk. A leader of one Bible study group once expressed a typical opinion saying, "What do scientists know anyway? I don't pay any attention to them."

Church leaders often say "your faith should not be in the wisdom of men, but in the power of God," and that is true.[8] But they ignore the fact that science is really nature revealing itself to us through controlled experiments. This means science is a different class of worldly wisdom from ordinary human philosophy. Real science is not a collection of educated speculations that find some general agreement, like political opinion. Scientific theories have a substance in reality, a numerical correspondence with the way things really are.

This is why the real enemy of the Church is not science, but the atheistic worldviews that are supposedly based in science. Saint Paul made it clear there is no sacred or innately profane thing: "nothing is unclean in itself."[9] Nature is from God, since He spoke the world into existence through His physical laws. Therefore, the cold hard facts of science are essentially the revealed words of God, to the degree we are able to comprehend. Science produces true physical knowledge and, as the saying goes, such knowledge is power.

Others say the Bible contains all the knowledge God wants us to have. But the Psalms say of the heavens, "Day unto day utters speech, and night unto night reveals knowledge. There is no speech nor language where their voice is not heard."[10] Surely, God intends that we learn about Him and ourselves from nature.

If you say "I don't believe that science has the truth," you may be happy to disbelieve science in favor of a particular view of Genesis, and you have settled the matter for yourself. It is true that salvation does not depend on science, but what about your children? In this age of information, people realize that scientific theories are backed by an abundance of evidence. This is especially true of young people, and they are leaving the faith in increasing numbers, persuaded by those who refute the faith on a seemingly scientific basis.

We should be willing to accept new ideas even if they are uncomfortable, so long as they are true. In Isaiah God said, "Behold, I am doing a new thing; now it springs forth, do you not perceive it?"[11]

Of course, the Church offers such a great salvation, and we do not have to make church into a science lesson. However, what we say about science should be physically true. Science does not make faith more real, but it does keep faith from irrationality. The world does not know it is spiritually dead, but it does have a level of knowledge about the physical world that it uses for measuring our credibility. Intelligent people with honest questions about God will not be very inclined to listen to spiritual truth, if what the Church says about the physical world is not true.

Young Earth Christians argue that scientific findings can't be put on the same plane as God's Word, but they are in danger of rejecting the revelation of God's Word in nature. They argue that science is imperfect, that it is done by human beings, and that it continually revises its theories and ideas. Young Earth Christians believe that most of what they find objectionable in science will disappear one day, but this is a vain hope.

The main features of today's scientific landscape are founded in the experiments and research of more than 400 years of discovery. Though we still have some very fundamental things to find out about the universe, it is not likely that any of the principal ideas in science today will be upended. There may well be theories that make a more complete accounting of nature, but current theories will almost certainly turn out to be a subset, or a special case, of a higher natural law.

Certainly I sympathize with believers that struggle with atheistic scientific claims that are at odds with Christianity. I grappled alone with these very doubts and apprehensions for many years. I was horrified, for a time, that atheists might be right about disproving God's existence. But, the truth is that science can buttress our faith if we can accept it.

I hasten to add not all science news can be believed. Mistakes, retractions and misrepresentations have been rising sharply, even in the most prestigious science journals.[12] Postmodernism is already taking a toll on science, and there is a growing sense that some scientific issues have become highly politicized. The hype over global warming is a prime example of this.[13]

Actually, global warming began when the last ice age ended before the industrial age. It is a good thing it did, or our complex society would likely not be here. In fact, global warming has also been occurring on Mars at least since the 1970's, and the polar caps there have been receding.[14, 15] This points to the Sun as a driver for part of the current warming of the Earth.

A new study from Columbia University shows that higher atmospheric carbon caused a global greening 120,000 years ago. At that time CO^2 levels were about 450 parts per million, while today they are 415 parts per million, and rising. During the Eocene period about 55 million years ago, carbon was 600 parts per million, or higher. The Arctic and Antarctica were both subtropical with palm trees.[16] These climate peaks and the intervening ice ages occurred over eons, without human influence.

In the current era, NASA satellite data indicates that, "a quarter to a half of the planet's vegetated lands have seen increases in leaf volume on trees and plants since about 1980."[17] This recent global greening is attributed to increased atmospheric CO_2, and it clearly does not portend the end of civilization. I am not saying that we do not need a clean environment, but I do mean to say that the benefits of "going green" and the dire predictions of catastrophe are inaccurate. More than 1600 top scientists like Freeman Dyson and John Clauser agree; a climate emergency does not exist.[18, 19, 20]

Accepting truth from science is not compromising with the world, as some would charge. It is simply accepting physical evidence from the best scientific research, revealing God's law in nature. Solomon commended the pursuit of knowledge in Proverbs 25:2, where he said, "the glory of kings is to search things out."[21] Saint Peter would remind us to have good reasons for our faith, and Hosea 4:6 says, "My people are destroyed for lack of knowledge."[22]

Jesus also respected the human need for physical evidence when He said to Thomas, "Put your finger here, and see my hands; and put out your hand, and place it in my side. Do not disbelieve, but believe."[23] Essentially, Christ endorsed the idea that people study nature, make observations, and profit from the information, even in matters of faith and the resurrection.

Therefore, I believe God ordains the pursuit of scientific truth. Indeed, God predicted the information age through the prophet Daniel, when he wrote, "many shall run to and fro (travel), and knowledge shall be increased."[24]

If believers accept the truth from science it does not put the Bible in a second class position. Science and the Bible deal with different fields of thought and experience. God's word remains unchanged. However, if we can accept scientific facts, fewer people will be hindered by the Church. More people may be willing to examine the evidence for Christianity and be drawn to the real life that God has to offer. With regard to science we should be as Christ said, "wise as serpents and innocent as doves."[25]

INFORMED INTERPRETATION

The Bible was not intended to be a book of science. It conveys moral and spiritual truth through a historical narrative of God's interactions with real people, and it was written with an ancient mindset. Nevertheless, the Church has always held that God's word in scripture can help us interpret nature, and guide our use of science. Indeed, Christianity's philosophical foundation enabled the birthing of science.

On the other hand, if the laws of nature are products of God's Word, science should be able to inform our interpretation of scripture where it impinges on the physical, and this is a small portion of scripture to be sure. Intelligent readers interpret every nonfiction narrative in this way, judging by the context of the whole work, and what they know from nature. Certainly, a generous allowance must be made for figures of speech, since the Bible makes such frequent use of this device. There are also translation issues with a few key words in Genesis, the original meaning of which can be considered without changing scripture.

Atheists, and even some Christians like John H. Walton, would argue that it is folly to look for concord of the Bible and science.[26] They claim that writers like Hugh Ross and I are superimposing a modern scientific viewpoint onto a scripture that says nothing about cosmic origins. Some insist that the Bible should only be interpreted with the limited view of the ancients. This strikes me as a uniquely modern idea, and an unnecessary encumbrance in interpreting scripture.

The language of Genesis 1 clearly does speak of cosmic origins. Both ancient Christian and Jewish expositors agree on this point. To my mind, it is inescapable that an informed interpretation of scripture, and God's Word in nature should be consistent in general detail. Physical truth from science necessarily reveals to us something of the Divine. Francis Schaeffer coined the phrase "true truth", which is truth that really exists, or a fact having its own autonomous reality.[27] True truth works philosophically, physically and morally. So, if the unbiased message from nature contradicts a few of our minor beliefs, it is worth considering more sophisticated interpretations of the few Bible verses that touch on physical truth.

GALILEO'S TALE OF WOE

Actually, our views of nature and the universe have always informed our faith, but not always in constructive ways, as the woeful tale of Galileo's astronomy reveals. Galileo provides a poignant and infamous example of Christianity adapting to new knowledge from science that ought to instruct us now. History shows that eventually Christians will come to accept those theories from science that are on a solid physical foundation, even if those theories are presently vehemently rejected.

The ancients before Galileo knew that the planets had different patterns of motion in the night sky than the other stars, tracing convoluted backtracking paths around the Earth. But they had no idea why. As the scripture says, "There is one glory of the sun, another glory of the moon, and another glory of the stars; for one star differs from another star in glory."[28] Still, everything in the heavens seemed to move around the Earth, which was by all appearances the center of the universe. This was the respected view from the time of the Greek philosopher Aristotle.[29]

Unfortunately, it is a fact that the true nature of the universe is often very counter-intuitive, and the example of the Sun-centric solar system is a rather tame one. In 1610, Galileo began looking into the heavens with his own telescope, and what he saw radically changed the authoritative view of the heavens and the Earth.

Galileo saw that the Moon's familiar surface features were actually vast planes, mountains and craters. He realized it had a natural surface like the Earth, and was subject to natural forces. He was the first to notice that Saturn has a system of rings and that Jupiter has four large moons that go around it in a periodic way. Galileo discovered the visual proof, in the phases of Venus, that Venus goes around the Sun, and that the Earth is not the center of the solar system, just as Copernicus had predicted mathematically. In fact, Galileo's measurements of the heavens were so precise that Sir Isaac Newton later used them in 1687 to formulate his laws of motion.[30]

The real nature of the solar system was a huge point of contention, and it is hard for us to appreciate just how big a shift in thinking this really was for some people at the time. Leaders of philosophy in the Church hotly debated the nature of the heavens, pitting Copernicus and Galileo against Aristotle. Many actually sided with a solar-centric view, but as you may know, when Galileo published his work on the true order of the solar system in 1632, he was put on trial for suspicion of heresy. Under this pressure Galileo recanted his work and lived out the rest of his days under house arrest.[31]

Some of Galileo's opponents pointed to Psalm 119:90 and 1 Chronicles 16:29-30 as evidence that a solar-centric solar system was not biblical. 1 Chronicles says, "Worship the LORD in the splendor of holiness; tremble before Him, all the Earth, yes, the world is established; it shall never be moved."[32] The phrase "it shall never be moved" was taken to mean that the Earth was literally fixed in space, being the center of all things in the heavens, but the medieval interpretation of the biblical text was incorrect.

Over time Galileo's observations, and the science of Copernicus, Kepler and Newton, unseated the old incorrect views of the heavens, even in the Church. Who now could take the old interpretation of the 1 Chronicles scripture seriously, or believe that Galileo's solar system is a stumbling block to the Christian faith? It is easy to see that this Bible passage simply means that God is to be worshiped, and that the Earth cannot be moved from His presence.

Eventually, the Church admitted its mistake, and Pope John Paul II finally cleared Galileo's name, embracing science unambiguously in the process. Going further on a separate occasion, Pope John Paul II also said "new findings lead us toward the recognition of evolution (change in biological systems over time) as more than a hypothesis" since there is evidence supporting it. "The theory proves its validity by the measure to which it can be verified."[33] Then in November 2005, the Vatican reaffirmed the idea that "the faithful should listen to what modern science has to offer."[34]

The Catholic Church even has its own Pontifical Academy of Science that seriously explores scientific matters. Membership has included the physicist Stephen Hawking of the University of Cambridge; David Baltimore, biologist and former President of Cal Tech; and Francis Collins, head of the Human Genome project. Past members also include the giants of quantum physics, Max Planck, Niels Bohr, Werner Heisenberg, Paul Dirac, Erwin Schrödinger and many others.[35] As Saint Paul suggests, "we cannot do anything against the truth, but only for the truth." [36] So it is ironic that our brothers and sisters in the Catholic Church are embracing truth from science well ahead of the Protestant Church.

For decades churches have been trying to reach more people by changing worship styles, and softening their message while trying to maintain correct doctrine. This strategy has only been moderately successful with the young people it was meant to attract. Over half of those between 25 and 40 years of age no longer follow the Christian faith. We must address the deeper questions and doubts that keep so many people from coming to God's eternal solution.

On the other side, liberal theologians have tried to modernize the Church by denying large chunks of scripture, based on naturalism. They adopt secular philosophies that are antithetical to Christianity, and for this cause many churches are dying on the vine—the vine being Christ Himself.

It is inescapable then that our physical worldview will influence how we interpret scripture. When our ideas about science are wrong, as in Galileo's time, Christians will surely have greater difficulty relating to the modern world. Accepting God's wisdom in His Word, and in nature, can help restore the place of the Church to the culture in a way that changes of style cannot.

Some will see accepting ideas from evolution or cosmology as a slippery slope, but there can be no more slippery slope than accepting something that is not true. The truth is that all real science today is just as benign to the Christian faith as the facts of the solar system, though it does not now seem that way to many believers. I am persuaded that science does not contradict any tenet of orthodox Christianity.

We Christians do not need to be afraid of any line of honest inquiry, or any scientific discovery. We should, to paraphrase a saying of Christ, "Render unto science what is of science." Indeed, modern science can be a bulwark for Christianity, even as it provides a new language to communicate the gospel to scientifically minded people.

A good place to start looking for God's proof marks in nature is in the heavens, where modern science really began. Look to the heavens which reveal the glory of the God who is really there. Yahwah Shammah.[37]

CHAPTER TWO

THE GLORY IN THE HEAVENS

"When I consider Your heavens, the work of Your fingers, the moon and the stars, which You have ordained, what is man that You are mindful of him?" ~ Psalms 8:3-4, New King James Version

There is a glory of God in the heavens that all people can witness. A deep dark night sky full of stars seen from a mountain top inspires me with awe, and a sense of God's presence that I find in very few circumstances. Forest Home Christian Camp in the mountains of southern California is such a place. There you can see many more stars than in the light-polluted lowlands. I recall one night there, looking up at the brilliant stars and the Milky Way. I was taking in God's wonder and majesty, and thinking about each point of light as a massive burning star—that God created all of it, from the highest heaven right down to me. I felt as though God was leaning down to touch me.

In Psalm 8, when King David marveled at the heavens and the relative insignificance of mankind, he was expressing a thoroughly modern view. Most scientists were so impressed with the universe that they used to say the universe has always been here; that it simply existed for all time. This seemed to agree with early 'static' observations of the heavens. Strict materialists were thus able to avoid the 'embarrassing' notion of a Creator.

Then discoveries in the early 20th century changed the scientific perspective of the heavens forever. Science discovered physical evidence of the Genesis account of creation.

HUBBLE, STARS, BLACK HOLES AND A BIT OF ME

In 1929 Edward Hubble discovered that a great many stars, or nebula, were actually distant galaxies—island universes. Each contained billions of stars and was separated from our own galaxy by millions of light years of relatively empty space. Scientists were amazed when he discovered that most other galaxies are moving away from us, meaning that the universe—space itself—is expanding. Moreover, Hubble found that the more distant the galaxy, the greater is its velocity away from our solar system. This is the underlying evolution of space. This expansion implies that the material of all the galaxies was collected together in the distant past. It implies the universe had an origin, as in Genesis 1.

We now know that our own star, the Sun, has its own orbit in an outer portion of the Milky Way galaxy, and that there are billions of other galaxies similar to our own. Each one has its own enormous population of stars. Scientists estimate that there are 400 billion stars in our galaxy alone. Astronomers have only cataloged a small portion of the stars in existence. There is no device, or method available that can count, or even see them all.

Just as the scripture says in Hebrews, there are countless stars in the heavens, "Therefore from one man (Abraham), and him as good as dead, were born as many as the stars of the sky in multitude— innumerable as the sand which is by the seashore."[1] Scientists now estimate there are approximately 10^{24} stars, about the same number as the sands of the seas.[2]

In low Earth orbit, Edward Hubble's namesake, the Hubble Space Telescope has revolutionized astronomy. My first big JPL project was supporting the vibration test activities on the Wide Field Planetary Camera (WFPC) for this telescope. The camera system vibration test was directed by our group's principle engineer, Terry Scharton. I was fortunate to have been mentored by Terry, working with him on numerous vibration tests over the course of several years. He was a charismatic innovator and the best engineer I ever knew.

WFPC would be installed in the huge Hubble Space Telescope and launched into Earth orbit by the Space Shuttle. In space this JPL camera system revealed that the telescope's primary mirror had been ground with an incorrect prescription. A system optics test could have revealed the problem before launch. Instead, it would take years of planning, a corrective optics design, and a risky spacewalk to upgrade Hubble to the performance it was supposed to have.

WFPC gave me the opportunity to lead regular test planning meetings, comprised of a team that was much more experienced than myself. I felt a little intimidated, though the older engineers seemed to enjoy showing me the ropes. Being an introvert by nature, I had to overcome my natural reticence to stand out, and demonstrate that I could tackle the technical issues.

My father was outspoken, and he was at times a harsh disciplinarian, as was common in the day. I retreated as a kid in order to keep peace with him, and I deliberately eschewed authority. I did not want to inflict similar injustices on other people. But I imitated dad in other ways. I adopted his work ethic which drove me to achieve as much as I could, meet new challenges, and better myself by stretching beyond my comfort zone. Mother and dad raised us in a Bible believing Lutheran church, with a good moral foundation. My parent's high standards prepared me for a career in a demanding high tech environment. Coming out of my shell, bit by bit, did not come naturally, but by taking reasonable risks in work and social situations, putting myself 'out there'.

In Junior High School, I had my first summer job, while my father had two jobs to bring in extra money. Mom and dad started with very little, but they worked hard to make a comfortable life for us. In the evening dad was a supervisor at a paper box plant, but during the day he had an unskilled job at a small pallet factory in my hometown.

I had not been getting along with my father for some time, so I was blessed to be able to work directly with him for two summers at the pallet factory. One job we had was cutting open enormous paper rolls for the local 3M plant, to prepare them for recycling.

Because of my father's excellent reputation, we were left to ourselves pretty much all day, preparing paper rolls for 3M. My father taught me how to use a power saw to cut the paper rolls open, and I began to see that he really did love me. Our relationship obtained a new tenderness and, for this reason, this was my most cherished work experience. Working with dad those two summers brought peace between us.

After two years my dad had a new job and he stopped working at the pallet factory, and he built a new home just outside of town. My summer job wasn't at all the same after that. I was on my own and the work became bone jarringly boring. By then, I was glad to be enrolled in university to become an engineer, to work with my mind.

As it turned out, the Jet Propulsion Laboratory would eventually be the perfect organization in which to grow, to gradually become more assertive in my conduct, and rescript my aversion of authority. In the 1980's people used to joke that JPL was a country club, a place to goof off, but this was a misconception. I never knew any group of tough minded engineers that worked harder, or smarter than the engineers at JPL. It was a stimulating environment.

In time I began to realize that most leaders at JPL were different than the typical honcho. Managers led by example, not by brute force. They delegated authority with the full expectation that each engineer would step up and accomplish the job at hand. Blame was rarely discussed, even though there were always problems threatening mission budgets and schedules. The paramount aim was to learn from mistakes, do the right thing, get the job done and achieve the mission's goals. This is how the laboratory ran the WFPC camera program.

Because of Hubble Space Telescope, the universe's majesty seems all the more miraculous, now that we understand the real nature of stars, and the vast volume and complexity of the heavens. Hubble has captured the wonder of creation, as new stars form within giant dust clouds, like in the Eagle Nebula and Helix Nebula. Such planetary nebulae formed when giant stars blew off the material of their outer shells, after burning most of their hydrogen fuel. These dust clouds contain the elements of worlds to come.

Fledgling stars and planetary systems are forming in the Eagle Nebula in droves. Stars are seen at various stages of birthing, and many are still enshrouded in planetary dust clouds. Some new giant stars are seen burning with so much pressure that they are pushing the dust away from other newly minted stars, making them look like comets with tails. I believe these images reveal God's creative hand in action, as it says in Psalms, "He determines the number of the stars; He gives to all of them their names."[3]

One of the key parameters in understanding space, stars, and galaxies is distance. As it says in Jeremiah, "It is He who made the earth by His power, who established the world by His wisdom, and by His understanding stretched out the heavens."[4]

Even the closest stars, the three stars comprising the Alpha Centauri system, are 4.5 light years away. The brightest of the three, Alpha Centuri A, is very much like our Sun. It takes 4.5 Earth years for light to travel from Alpha Centauri to Earth, so on Earth we are seeing what the Alpha Centuri system looked like 4.5 years ago.

There is no earthly way of knowing what is going on at Alpha Centauri at this moment. When astronomers look into space they are really looking back in time, which is why they use the light year as a measure of the great distances of space. A light year quantifies the idea that we are looking into the past along a specific distance. This way of thinking about the vast distances of space provided the first clue that time and space are part of the same fabric. You can't have one without the other.

Distances to nearby stars have been calculated by means of trigonometry and precise measurements of star positions, with the Earth on either side of its orbit around the Sun.[5] There is no guessing involved in these distances; only measurements of angles and high school level math are required. This direct measurement of stellar distances has been used on hundreds of stars, out to about 500 light years.

Direct distance measurements and the intrinsic brightness of certain types of nearby stars make it possible for astronomers to use those stars as source intensity references. In other words, a reference star of a particular mass and brightness can be used to determine the distances of similar stars, that are too distant to measure directly.

Cepheid stars are such source references, examples of which are close enough for direct distance measurement. In 1912, Henrietta Leavitt discovered a correlation of the pulsing rate and intrinsic brightness of Cepheid stars, allowing them to be used as a reference stellar candle for deep space distance measurements. She discovered that the brightness of a Cepheid star increases and wanes regularly, as the pressure of the nuclear fire within pushes the star's surface outward, until the star's own immense gravity pulls the surface back in. A

Cepheid's known brightness can be used to extrapolate distances to more distant stars, even stars in distant galaxies out to millions of light years with high reliability.[6]

Looking into deeper space is challenging technically, because light from the most distant stars and galaxies is extremely faint. This is best done with space-based observatories. Space observatories avoid the light absorption and scattering of the Earth's atmosphere, where density perturbations (or air turbulence), light pollution, and air pollution make it difficult to resolve faint objects in deep space. Such observations necessarily involve photographic exposures that can last tens of hours, requiring exquisitely precise pointing and the digital stitching together of multiple exposures.

The range to very distant galaxies is measured using the "red shift" of the light coming from those galaxies. If a star, or galaxy is moving away from Earth, the light still reaches us at the speed of light, but its light waves are more stretched out. This causes a color shift in the light toward the red end of the light spectrum. This shift can be used to determine how fast a distant star is moving from the Earth. The faster an object moves from Earth, the more its light is stretched out, or shifted toward the red side of the light spectrum, hence the term "red shift".

Conversely, light from stars moving toward us is color shifted toward the blue end of the visible spectrum. The light from these stars appears bluer than light from a star that is stationary relative to Earth. It is like the sound from a train horn that has a high pitch as the train approaches, but as the train passes by and recedes in the distance, the horn sound pitch becomes lower. Light and sound waves are exactly analogous in this way. The amount of blue, or red shift of a star's light spectrum is therefore a measure of how fast a star is moving toward us, or away from us.

All material elements, hydrogen, oxygen, iron, and the like, have unique light signatures when heated to a high enough temperature. These signatures can be precisely measured using a spectrometer. Stars are predominantly composed of hydrogen, and the hydrogen heated in the Sun produces the same color signature, or spectrum, as hydrogen heated in a science lab. So scientists can measure how red, or blue shifted the hydrogen light signature is from distant stars or even galaxies. The distance to these stars in light years can be inferred from their red shift using Hubble's law.

Distance measurements in the billions of light years are made by observing exploding stars called Supernova, that emit enough energy to be seen across most of the universe. Mario Livio, a senior astrophysicist at the Hubble Space Telescope Science Institute, has made such measurements. Using the red shift of Supernovae, Livio's team established the age of the universe as 13.7 billion years—an amazingly old age.[7] This was done using the Hubble Space Telescope, and the most advanced adaptive optics telescopes on Earth.

Supernovae pose an extinction danger to life forms on any poorly situated planets. An extraordinary image taken by Hubble Space Telescope shows the Eta Carinae star system, which is expelling giant dust clouds in two lobes. One of the largest known stars at more than 100 solar masses, it resides within the billowing dust cloud. Eta Carinae's eruption was first observed in 1843, and scientists believe it could go supernova—explode—at any time.[8] There is some suggestion that distant exploding stars may have influenced the climate on Earth and changed the course of life here. Thankfully, there doesn't seem to be a supernova waiting to detonate near the Earth—Eta Carinae is 7,500 light years away. God has been watching out for us.

Quasars are pulsing energy sources at the centers of certain distant galaxies, and are some of the most energetic objects in the universe. Quasar energy pulses are most likely generated as massive amounts of material spiral into a galaxy's central black hole. This process propels enormous jets of energy and material into space. The red shift of Quasar sources can be used to measure galactic distances of many billions of light years. In this way, Quasars can be seen as ancient signs of the Creator's fierce and immeasurable power.

A star of 10 solar masses, or more, may eventually become a black hole, packing all its mass into a volume the size of a small city. Massive black holes can only be observed by their gravitational influence on nearby stars, and by the super-heated material that spirals into the black hole. The high concentration of mass within a black hole creates an extremely high gravitational attraction, that not even light can escape, hence the name black hole.

The black hole's "event horizon" is the spherical boundary between the normal universe and the black hole. This horizon is the last place in the universe where matter, or even light, can avoid being consumed by the black hole. Neither ingested matter nor light can escape once it crosses the event horizon. Any star, or planet that meets up with a black hole is therefore in a dreadful situation.

Intriguingly, a black hole is more like hell than anything else in the universe. It is an inescapable place of utter darkness, isolation, and gravitational bondage. Jesus described this kind of place in Luke, "between us (in heaven) and you (in hell) a great chasm has been fixed, in order that those who would pass from here to you may not be able, and none may cross from there to us."[9] Now, I do not think that black holes really have anything to do with hell, but they are analogous to the biblical hell—a storehouse for evil that cannot be escaped.

The most distant galaxies ever imaged were observed in a novel way. Galaxies at 13 billion light years distant have been photographed using a natural gravitational lens effect, predicted by Albert Einstein. The gravity of a massive galaxy will bend light coming from an even more distant galaxy, concentrating the light like a lens for a favorably positioned observer on Earth. Instances of gravitational lensing have made it possible to observe galaxies that would otherwise be too faint, and too far away to see. So the focusing power of one immense galaxy, or group of galaxies, can help us see another more distant one.

ALIEN PLANETS SIGHTED

The Hubble Telescope has been upgraded twice by space walking astronauts to improve its performance. Hubble was manufactured with a defective optical prescription, and the uncorrected Hubble was launched into space without a system optics test. Wide Field Planetary Camera II was designed by JPL to correct Hubble's vision problem in visible light. In 1993, I conducted the acoustic test of this new camera. An acoustic test simulates the intense rocket noise of lift off, pressure waves that can cause hardware to vibrate severely. It is one of the most realistic mechanical tests that can be performed on flight hardware before it is launched into space.

Prior to the acoustic test, I traveled to Goddard Space Flight Center with Terry Scharton. We were there to measure the support structure impedance, in preparation for a mirror assembly vibration test. Typically acceleration alone is controlled during a vibration test, letting hardware forces peak wildly at times. Terry worked out a practical way to limit the forces at the hardware mounts, making vibration testing more realistic, and less hazardous for sensitive lightweight space hardware. Subsequent acoustic and vibration testing readied Hubble's new camera.

Once the Hubble Space Telescope was upgraded with Wide Field Planetary Camera II, it made the first direct observation of a planet around another star, Fomalhaut b. Hubble accomplished this even though it was not specifically designed to do this; an astonishing achievement.[10]

An earth-sized planet, with an earth-like gravity has also been discovered in its star's habitable zone for the first time—the planet Gliese 581, nearby in our Milky Way galaxy.[11] Gliese 581 is 20 light years away, and it is tidally locked with its parent star. This means the same side of the planet always faces its star, the same way the Moon's near side always faces Earth. For this reason, the habitable zone of the planet is a narrow region near the terminator—the boundary between the light and dark sides of the planet. The light side of the planet is too hot, and the dark side too cold to support life. The expectation is there are many similar planets that might support life, however distant.

The Kepler planet-finding observatory has identified more than 4000 confirmed planets, and counting.[12] Most all of these planets dwell in radiation environments so extreme—so close to their host stars—that life could not possibly exist there. By comparison, Earth is a wonder. Only a small handful of candidate habitable worlds are known, though newer planet finding telescopes are being developed to find other extraterrestrial planets.

Now on its third camera, Hubble is even more powerful, and it will be able to peer near to the edge of the visible universe. The new James Webb space telescope has captured its first spectacular images, and it surpasses even Hubble. Earth-based telescopes have become more powerful too, and the best of them, like the Keck Observatory, have built-in adaptive optics technology to get around some of the limitations of viewing through the atmosphere.

Many people do not realize that we are living in the golden age of astronomy right now. We have discovered far more in space in the last few decades than was known in all the rest of human history.

In view of the countless galaxies and stars in the heavens, their various stages of development and the vast distances to those objects, there can be little doubt about the ancient age of the universe. In deep space, the immensity, complexity, and order of the universe reveal something of God's unbounded intellect, and His marvelous handiwork.

The terrible radiance and power of countless stellar nuclear furnaces and blazing quasars clearly display something of God's awesome glory and power. For me, the old age of the universe and its stability reflect the unchanging nature of the Ancient One.

CHAPTER THREE

THE EARTH, GENESIS & CIVILIZATION

"God called the dry land Earth, and the waters that were gathered together He called Seas. And God saw that it was good."
~ Genesis 1:10 ESV

Earth is the natural wonder of the known galaxy, and it is the only known island of sentient beings in the universe. The Earth is just right for human beings to develop, live and thrive. Our planet is very different from the others in our solar system, which are generally inhospitable to life. The favorable conditions for life on Earth are unique among the 4000 plus known planets. For me, it is not a stretch to say that the Earth is a miracle.

Contrary to conventional wisdom, the Bible's brief depictions of the Earth match the basics of what we know from science. Certainly, an allowance must be made for idioms like the "four corners of the earth," that are still in common use today. But, for example, Isaiah says, "God sits above the circle of the earth,"[1] and in Proverbs it says, "When He established the heavens, I was there; when He drew a circle on the face of the deep."[2] These ancient texts correctly imply an Earth with circular form, and with a physical place in the heavens. They also obviously employ figurative language.

What we know of the Earth and the solar system has, since 1958, increased exponentially largely due to a fleet of robotic spacecraft from the Jet Propulsion Laboratory and NASA.[3] The first American satellite was JPL's Explorer I, which orbited the Earth and discovered the Van Allan Radiation belt. This was closely followed by the Ranger probes to the Moon, and the Mariner spacecraft to Mercury, Venus and Mars. More recently, the Voyager and Galileo spacecraft reconnoitered the outer gas giant planets. The large robotic Cassini spacecraft has explored Saturn and its moons.

The planetary bodies in our star system are now known to be amazingly diverse. Understanding them is helping us better understand the Earth, and how to interpret information we are gathering of planets around other stars. As much as anything, the other planets of our solar system reveal just how unique the Earth is, reinforcing the notion of the Earth as a miracle.

GENESIS 1 AND COSMOLOGY

Let's examine how it is possible to reconcile the facts of planetary science with the account of Genesis, beginning with the heart of our system—the Sun. NASA has explored the Sun with the Pioneer, Ulysses, SoHo and ACE spacecraft, to name a few.

Our home star provides a full spectrum of light, that lifts our spirits even as it powers life on the planet. The Sun is a bright, stable and long-lived star, larger than most, and it is just the kind of star that is able to support a planet with life. Without it nothing could live on Earth.

Astonishingly, the Sun contains about 99.9% of the mass of the solar system. It is a nearly perfect sphere of hot hydrogen plasma (a hot form of matter) with a core so hot that it sustains a continuous process of nuclear fusion that converts hydrogen into helium. As a result, the temperature of the Sun's core runs in the tens of millions of degrees.

At 10,000°F, the surface of the Sun looks like a lake of fire, just like the biblical descriptions of hell. Even so, the Sun's gigantic magnetosphere, formed by its magnetic field, protects the Earth from energetic charged particles from deep space, like a magnetic deflector shield.

So how can the ancient text in Genesis relate to the science of cosmology? Genesis seems to introduce Earth with a glaring problem of timing. The Sun and Moon appear on day 4 of Genesis, well after the Earth has been created. It says, "Then God made two great lights: the greater light to rule the day, and the lesser light to rule the night. He made the stars also. God set them in the firmament of the heavens to give light on the earth."[4] Science tells us that the Earth formed after the Sun.

But there is a legitimate pre-science interpretation of the Genesis 1 text that eliminates this quandary. It says the Sun and Moon became visible from Earth on the "fourth" day. It is not that they were created out of the logical order.[5, 6]

Science tells us that the early Earth's sky was opaque, so that the Sun could not be seen from the Earth's surface. Over time, the atmosphere was transformed by massive amounts of plant life into an oxygen-rich, transparent atmosphere. This transition to a transparent atmosphere made it possible for the Sun, the Moon and the stars to be seen from Earth's surface for the first time, clearly marking day from night, and the seasons. I believe this Earth-centric event is the one noted on Genesis day 4. The oxygen rich atmosphere also made it possible for larger animals to live on Earth.

There is also the famous problem of the length of "days" in the Genesis 1 account. The Bible does not give an age for the universe. It was not germane to the Genesis account of God's creation of the universe, and Adam's fall. The scientific evidence, and the most reasonable biblical interpretation, is that the days of Genesis were very long periods of time, not 24 hour days.

The old age of the Earth is revealed by various methods. For instance, layers in the Earth's ice core samples drilled in Antartica reach back 2.7 million years. Older ice cores will surely be found as more core drilling is performed.[7]

Radioactive elements provide a record of radioactive decay stretching back for billions of years. Radioactive elements decay at predictable rates. Some decay very quickly, in fractions of a second, while other elements decay over the course of many millions of years. Of all the possible radioactive elements (nuclides) 18 are found naturally on Earth. Kenneth Miller describes what they reveal about the age of the Earth, "Every nuclide with a half-life of less that 80 million years is missing from our region of the solar system (*except for short lived nuclides that are produced continually by cosmic radiation, like Carbon-14*), and every nuclide with a half-life of greater than 80 million years is present. ... There is a reason that the short lived nuclides are no longer around, and the reason is obvious: The solar system is much older than 80 million years. In the billions of years since its formation, the short-lived nuclides have simply decayed themselves out of existence."[8]

In particular, advanced lead-uranium radioactive dating methods firmly place the age of the Sun and Earth at 4.5 billion years, roughly one third of the age of the universe.[9] Rocks gathered from the Moon by the Apollo astronauts confirmed this age for the Earth Moon system. Using similar methods, the earliest life forms on Earth date back at least 3.8 billion years. These ages are consistent with the most reasonable interpretation of "day" in Genesis as a long period of time.[10]

Linguistically, Genesis 1 uses a poetic form when referring to the days of creation. Gleason Archer, an expert in biblical languages, writes, "The Hebrew says, "And the evening took place, and the morning took place, day one" (verse 1:5). ...In Hebrew prose of this genre, the definite article was generally used where the noun was intended to be definite; only in poetic style could it be omitted. The same is true with the rest of the six days; they all lack the definite article. Thus they are well adapted to a sequential pattern, rather than to strictly delimited units of time (24 hour days)."[11]

Gerald Schroeder goes straight to the original meaning of the phrase 'evening and morning'. He writes, "The Hebrew word for evening is *erev*. The root of *erev* is disorder, mixture, chaos. The Hebrew word for morning is *boker*, its root being orderly, able to be discerned. In the subtle language of evening and morning, centuries before the Greek words of chaos and cosmos were ever written (Hebrew writing predates the Greek), the Bible described a step-by-step flow from disorder (*erev*) to order (*boker*); from the plasma of the big bang to the harmony of life."[12]

Psalm 90 is attributed to Moses, as is the book of Genesis. In that Psalm, Moses used a similar literary device of evening and morning, "You turn man to destruction... In the morning they are like grass which grows up: In the morning it flourishes and grows up; in the evening it is cut down and withers."[13] Here Moses was not referring to a 24 hour day, but to the span of a human life.

There are other textual problems with 24 hour days. It is not possible, in a literal sense, for the first three days of Genesis 1 to have 24 hour solar cycles, if you believe the Sun was not created until the forth day.

Fred Heeren points out that "Augustine said that the creation 'days' were not sun-divided days, but rather, Goddivided days. Others who believed that the creation days were not necessarily solar days include Irenaeus, second century apologist and martyr; Origen, third century apologist; Basil, 4th century bishop of Caesarea; and Thomas Aquinas, 13th century theologian. This tradition goes back to ancient Jewish thinking, for the position that the days of Genesis were not to be taken literally was also held by first- century Jewish writers, Philo and Josephus."[14]

Genesis 2:16-17 says, "And the Lord God commanded the man, saying, "Of every tree of the garden you may freely eat; but of the tree of the knowledge of good and evil you shall not eat, for in the day that you eat of it you shall surely die." Adam did not die on the specific day he disobeyed God, by eating the forbidden fruit, but he lived for several hundred more years, according to Genesis 5:5.[15] Here again, the word day in Genesis 2 was used in a figurative sense, for Adam did eventually die.

The culmination of the Bible's creation account is found in Genesis 2:4, "These are the *generations* of the heavens and of the earth when they were created, in the *day* that the LORD God made the earth and the heavens." Later, in Genesis 5:1 Moses wrote, "the book of the generations of Adam. In the *day* that God created man."[16] Here Genesis uses the word "day" in conjunction with "generations", clearly indicating long periods of time.

There are many reasons both biblical and scientific to take the days of the Genesis creation account as epochs. In this way, Genesis and science are seen to agree. The old age of the Earth reflects God's patience, His timelessness, and His dependability.

HOT WORLDS

A long hot "day" on Mercury is nearly as long as 59 Earth days. Mercury, the planet nearest the Sun, looks a great deal like the Earth's moon. It is a rocky and heavily cratered body with only 6 percent of the Earth's mass. Even though it is 28 million miles from the Sun, Mercury is so hot that what atmosphere it might have once had boiled away long ago. Surface temperatures there reach 800°F on the sunny side and plunge to –270°F on the dark side. The solar radiation on Mercury would be intense enough to cook you in no time at all. There is virtually no chance of life existing on hot and arid Mercury.

The next planet out from the Sun is Venus. It is the most like the Earth in size and rocky composition, with a mass of 82% of Earth's mass. Like Earth, Venus's surface has relatively few craters, having been resurfaced by volcanism, intense erosion, and tectonic forces.

Unlike the Earth, Venus has no natural moon, and it is just as hot as Mercury. The planet is blanketed by a nearly featureless opaque atmosphere that is 90 times as dense as Earth's, with temperatures higher than 860°F on the planet surface. These temperatures are due, in large part, to a closer orbit around the Sun, coupled with a dense atmosphere of 97% carbon dioxide. This is a poisonous greenhouse gas, that has intensified the temperatures on the planet.

Topographical images returned by the Magellan radar imaging spacecraft reveal that Venus probably once had Earth like water oceans, but they have long since boiled away. Instead of water, Venus now has sulfuric acid clouds high in its upper atmosphere. Its stormy atmosphere is so corrosive, and its temperature and pressure so high, that the probes that have been sent to land there have only functioned for a few minutes. The Russian landing craft Venera 13 managed to return only a few images from the hellish Venusian surface. The contrast with Earth's favorable atmosphere and location around the Sun could hardly be more stunning.

HOME SWEET HOME

Our exquisite home planet is the third from the Sun, and at 93 million miles, it is just the right distance from the Sun to keep water liquid in most places, over most of the year. If Earth were significantly closer to the Sun, or if it had significantly more CO_2, the atmosphere would heat up in a run away greenhouse effect like Venus. If the Earth's orbit ventured too far from the Sun, most water would be solid ice.

The Earth's orbit is nearly circular, so that the distance to the Sun only varies a few percent throughout the year. Consequently, seasonal temperatures don't fluctuate too widely.

This orbit is ideal for supporting life, which is why Earth is said to be in the "Goldilocks Zone" around the Sun. Earth could also be called the "Baby Bear" planet, because everything about it is just right. It is hard to conceive of a planet that is better suited to life, or that bears so many of God's proof marks.

Earth is the only planet in the solar system with significant amounts of liquid surface water, one of the most rare and precious substances in the universe. Three quarters of the surface of our planet is covered with liquid water!

THE BIBLE AND LIFE SCIENCE

Earth alone has a complete water cycle of evaporation, humidity, rain, rivers and oceans. Tellingly, the water cycle that produces rain was described in the Bible long before its modern discovery. David wrote in Psalms, "He (the LORD) causes the vapors to ascend from the ends of the earth; He makes lightning for the rain."[17] Job 36:27 plainly says, "He draws up drops of water, which distill as rain from the mist,"[18] describing invisible, but key features of the Earth's water cycle.

Actually, the existence of a compound like water is a greater miracle than a planet where everything is just right for life. Water has all the properties of mass, acid neutrality, liquidity, viscosity, and dissolving power necessary to make the biosphere work. It powers the fluids in individual cells, blood, nervous systems and digestive systems. In fact, two thirds of the human body consists of water.

The biosphere necessarily leads us to the epicenter of the controversy with atheism—evolution. It is pretty clear why the theory of evolution is so threatening to the Church. It is generally believed by atheists and Christians alike, that the theory of evolution is incompatible with the account of creation in Genesis. Darwinists say that evolution is entirely non-directed and random, and that there is no design in it. But the atheists and the anti-evolution believers are mistaken. Evolution as a process, is compatible with scripture and the Creator. It is the atheistic worldview that many infer from evolution that is at odds with Christianity, and not any facts from biology or paleontology.

In the strictest sense, evolution is simply the change in a system over time. Everything in the universe changes and has its own dynamics; nothing physical is truly static or unchanging. Trajectory equations describe the evolution of a cannon ball's path in flight. In biology, evolution is the study of changes in organisms over time. This necessarily involves reconstructing past events from fossils and DNA mutations. In the process, scientists have successfully integrated all the facts of the biosphere, and demonstrated how all species are related on a genetic level.

My intent here is not to recount the considerable scientific evidence for evolution, but to show that the physical theory does not contradict scripture. There are pre-science interpretations of Genesis by Jewish scholars that agree with modern science on this point. Many Christian theologians and scientists like John Polkinghorne, and Benjamin Warfield have also argued that evolution and the Bible are compatible. Others like Francis Collins, the head of the human genome project, and a Christian, have referred to this view as theistic evolution.[19]

Billy Graham, the greatest evangelist of the 20th century said this about evolution to David Frost, "I don't think that there's any conflict at all between science today and the Scriptures.... The Bible is not a book of science. The Bible is a book of Redemption, but of course, I accept the Creation story. I believe that God did create the universe. I believe He created man, and whether it came by an evolutionary process and at a certain point He took this person or being and made him a living soul, or not, does not change the fact that God did create man.... whichever way God did it makes no difference as to what man is and man's relationship to God."[20]

C.S. Lewis was one of the most prominent apologists of the 20th century. He had this to say about the creation of human beings, "For long centuries God perfected the animal form which was to become the vehicle of humanity and the image of Himself.... Then, in the fullness of time, God caused to descend upon this organism, both on its psychology and physiology, a new kind of consciousness which could say "I" and "me," which could look upon itself as an object, which knew God, which could make judgments of truth, beauty, and goodness, and which was so far above time that it could perceive time flowing past."[21]

Ironically, evolution is not without precedence in God's revelation. We know for sure that mankind's relationship with God and the Holy Scriptures have evolved over time. The Bible details the history of Adam and Eve, the first living souls who walked with God. It chronicles their fall, and their fractured family, and the enduring separation of mankind from God. As time passed, God made a faith covenant with Abraham, that he would father the nation of Israel and be a blessing to the world.

After Abraham's descendants became enslaved in Egypt, God raised up Moses. He was a Hebrew man who was educated by the Egyptians, and whom God called powerful in speech and action. God used Moses to deliver the nation of Israel out of slavery in Egypt, thus fulfilling His promise to Abraham. God then gave Moses the law. The Jews call this Torah, and by it He forged the nation of Israel. The law established universal moral standards which were adopted by all Western governments, until recently.

Finally, Israel's law and religious practices created the context for the coming of Jesus Christ. For centuries the scriptures comprised only the law and the prophets, showing us our inadequacy before God. Then Christ came in the flesh, fulfilling many Old Testament prophecies. He was targeted for death because He claimed to be God's Son. Yet, He gave Himself over to death willingly, to make us acceptable to God. This was foretold hundreds of years in advance by Moses, Isaiah, Daniel, Micah, king David and other prophets. These prophecies prove that every detail of Jesus Christ's terrible death was planned and ordained by God. Daniel even foretold the specific time in history that Messiah would appear, adding that He would be cut off, but not for Himself. After His resurrection from the dead, His disciples wrote the books of the New Testament. In this way, Christ forever changed our relationship with God, and our understanding of the prophets.

Then, in 1948, God reestablished the Jewish nation in the land of Israel, just as the prophets Moses, Ezekiel and Isaiah predicted, proving that He still directs events in history. This came to pass after Israel's dispersal 2000 years ago, and despite the many tyrants who have tried to eradicate the Jewish people.

Evil rulers have done this attempting to destroy God's promises to the Jews, and thus make void the word of God. Instead, by God's hand, the Jews as a nation have repeatedly survived their more powerful contemporaries, who have disappeared from the stage of history.

So God has deliberately moved humanity through a spiritual evolution that is similar to biological evolution. The distinction is that the 2000 year long evolution of scripture was clearly directed by God. It was marked by increasing spiritual knowledge and grace, gradually improving many human societies in the process. By this, God's promise to bless all nations through Abraham has been fulfilled. God's direction in biological evolution has been less obvious and unannounced.

So how can the Bible be reconciled with evolution? Genesis 1 lays out a progression of material creation, then plant life, lower animal life forms, and then higher forms of life, just as described by science.

At first glance, Genesis 2:5 onwards presents a different sequence of events from Genesis 1, but Genesis 2 is not about chronology or processes. Genesis 2:8, and later Genesis 2:15 both say that God put the man, whom He had formed, in the Garden. Genesis 2:15 simply restates what God had done in verse 2:8. The 'forming' of the animals in Genesis 2:19 recalls their prior creation in Genesis 1. Adam was not created before the animals, as Genesis 1 makes clear. I don't believe he was placed in the Garden twice, and animals were not created a second time. The repetition is used for emphasis, as it frequently is in the Bible. Genesis 2 is about the interactions of Adam, Eve and their Creator.

Genesis 2:7 uses the metaphor of God forming man from "the dust of the ground." Genesis 1:11–24 explains the process leading to that event; God successively commanded the earth and the seas to bring forth plants, and increasingly complex living creatures.[22] The word creation was not used here. Instead life was commanded to arise in a multitude of forms, through a process not specified in the Bible.

It is logical to conclude from the Genesis text, and by what we know from science, that Earth brought forth diverse life forms through a series of morphology changes. Indeed, the ascent of life forms described in Genesis 1 reads like the natural process that we now call evolution—a complex progression from lower to higher life forms, arising within the ecosystem, driven by God's commands to the earth and the seas. Jesus attributed a similar God given power to the earth when He said, "if a man should scatter seed on the ground... and the seed should sprout and grow, he himself does not know how. For the earth yields crops by itself."[23]

The fossil and DNA evidence is that God created human beings from a chimpanzee lineage. The life and death of thousands of generations of creatures were involved in this process, over the course of millions of years. You may believe that God would never create mankind from apes, because we are made in His image, and apes are not. But this is really just a question of raw materials, 'earth' versus apes that arose from the earth. Revelation 13:11 uses 'earth' in the latter sense in predicting the coming of a man known as the antichrist, "Then I saw another beast *rising out of the earth*." Jewish blessings like the Hamotzi use a similar phraseology, "Blessed are You, O Lord our God, King of the Universe, who brings forth bread *from the earth*."[24]

I use the term evolution here strictly to denote the scientific description of biological processes, and not in a way to exclude the Creator from the stream of events. Genesis 1 says that God directed these natural processes, which it describes correctly in general terms. God foreknew that these processes would eventually lead to you, and me, specifically, in a miracle of grand scale.[25]

Over time I began to interpret Adam and Eve as allegorical characters, but now I take them as real persons in the stream of history. The Bible says God breathed a new kind of soul life into the nostrils of a man, whom He had already formed.[26] Genesis 2:7 says, "And the LORD God formed man of the dust of the ground." After the man was formed through an unspecified process, God "breathed into his nostrils the breath of life; and man became a living soul." In other words, there was a human 'animal' that God chose to make into a complete human being named Adam.

Gerald Schroeder writes that, "There is no biblical problem with human-looking creatures predating Adam. As Talmudic and ancient commentaries point out, they were animals with human shapes but lacking the *neshama* (soul life) ... that changed an animal, amoral Adam into an Adam with moral responsibility. ... the *Adam* became a communicating spirit (Genesis 2:7)."[27] Christian Bible scholars Richard Fischer, Gleason Archer and others agree with this view.[28] Adam began to look beyond physical needs, towards self reflection, community and writing; the requisites of civilization.

It is consistent with the Bible, then, to believe that a great many pre-human contemporaries of Adam would have been living outside the Garden of Eden. These creatures were the same biological species as Adam, but they did not have the new soul life.

Such a human lineage should not bother Christians. It is our spirit that is made in God's image, rather than our physical form of arms, legs, torso and a head.[29] It is said that Jesus "did not count equality with God a thing to be grasped, but emptied himself, by taking the form of a servant, being born in the likeness of men."[30] Jesus "emptied Himself" to be contained, as it were, within an earthly human form. The Psalmist adds that we shall, one day, bear an even greater likeness of God than we do now, in the life to come: "I shall be satisfied when I awake in Your likeness."[31]

Evolution is an earthy, gritty and indirect process from a human viewpoint, and you may not like the way God made the world, or the raw materials He used to make us. But as God told Job, "Where were you when I laid the foundations of the earth? Tell Me, if you have understanding."[32] It took me many years to warm up to the idea of evolution, so I understand the reticence among believers to accept the theory. Yet we know we are all born into the world in a rather earthy way. So it is with evolution.

Of course there are mysteries in evolution to be solved. Aside from harmful deformities, morphology changes have never been directly observed and it is still a mystery how new species arise. Famously, Genesis 1:13 states that life reproduces "according to its kind."[33] This refers to the genetic and reproductive stability within each species, and we know first hand that animals and plants reproduce in this way. There are many animals, like certain turtles, sharks, crocodiles and alligators that have changed little during their long tenure on Earth.

The Tuatara is a lizard-like living fossil that is virtually unchanged since the dinosaurs roamed the Earth. Yet its DNA, the unique molecular information required to grow any plant, or animal, is changing at an unusually high rate.[34] The Coelacanth is a large primitive-looking fish with limb-like fins. It is a transitional animal that primarily has fish attributes, but it bears live young. Once thought extinct for 65 million years, the Coelacanth's form has remained unchanged for 400 million years and it lives to this day.[35]

There are still older life forms, single cell bacteria and algae, that have not changed since life began on Earth. It is believed that these simple algae arose at virtually the same time that water formed oceans on the Earth. Frank Tipler explains eloquently that, "Certain lines of cyanobacteria have not changed for over 3.5 billion years. This individual (identical individual copies) has been alive almost as long as the Earth itself has existed!"[36]

Many Christians think that the Genesis command of biological stability—animals reproducing "after their own kind"—excludes the possibility of natural morphology changes. To the contrary, biological stability complements God's other commands that the earth and the seas bring forth a multitude of life forms.

God did not seed the earth with signs of a progression that never happened, or the fossils of animals that never lived to fool us. Still living are biological links like mudskippers, transitional fish that can "walk" across the land to another water hole, and are able to spend days out of the water.[37] The lineage between living animals and ancient fossils is real, even though morphology changes are not fully understood. Similarities in the DNA of related species demonstrate that this is the case.

There are more significant mysteries in evolution as well. Life's sudden beginning is an embarrassment for evolutionary theory based solely in random chance. Life appeared on Earth immediately after the heavy bombardment by comets and asteroids ended, within a geological instant.[38] Mathematicians like Seth Lloyd have proven that random chance can never account for the genesis of even the simplest life forms, much less explain the increasing complexity of life forms.[39] The odds against life arising point unambiguously to a Creator. Still, if you care to accept it, the evolutionary evidence from fossils and DNA lend a level of complexity and depth to the poetry of the Genesis creation story that previous generations could not have appreciated.

Creationists do reasonably ask, "Why didn't God clearly tell us about evolution?" God answers this question in Proverbs: "It is the glory of God to conceal things, but the glory of kings is to search things out."[40] Obviously, God has not told us a great many things, and much has been out of common view like atoms and the true nature of planetary bodies.

Believers are right when they say that the Darwinist worldview is empty at its base, devoid of meaning or purpose, and that it is the antithesis of the Church's message of hope and eternal life. However, they make a crucial mistake by accepting the atheistic interpretation of evolution, instead of taking the scientific evidence of the process at face value.

ADAM & EDEN IN HISTORY

Famed Egyptologist David Rohl corroborates the historical veracity of the person of Adam and his clan, though he is not (yet) a Christian. He does this through a variety of extra biblical records and archeological evidence.[41] The founders of Mesopotamia's civilization were long remembered as gods, their deeds being recorded on thousands of clay cuneiform tablets. These long hidden historical records are still being deciphered by modern linguists. Rohl and Richard Fischer assert that the ancient Akkadian legend of Adapa is a secular account of the biblical Adam.[42] The Assyrian king Ashurbanipal also "traced his ancestry through his grandfather back to Asshur (son of Shem who built Nineveh) and to Adapa (Adam)."[43]

David Rohl locates Eden as a real place, in the region of Lake Van and Lake Uremia, an area that was subsequently called Ararat in the Bible. This is roughly at the border of present day Turkey and Iran, south of Armenia. Eden's territory was identified by tracking down the four rivers of Genesis 2 that have their headwaters in Eden, namely the rivers Euphrates, the Tigris, the Gaihun-Aras (Gihon) and the Kezel Uizhun (Pishon).[44]

Rohl then pinpoints the Garden within Eden, "It lies at the western end of the Adji Chay valley, near the city of Tabriz (of modern day Iran). The Garden is 'in the east of Eden' (*Genesis 2:8*) and is protected on its north, east and south sides by the high mountain peaks of the Savalan and Sahand ranges. To the west are the treacherous marshlands of the Adji Chay delta stretching out into Lake Uremia. The Adji Chay has an older name - the Median - which means "'walled-garden' - this is the river, described in Genesis 2:10, which waters the Garden of Eden."[45]

Many centuries later, Isaiah 37:12 and 2 Kings 19:12 refer to "the people of Eden," indicating Eden was still a populated place in their day, though without God's Garden.

After Adam's expulsion from the Garden, he and his clan moved westward to an area south of the Zargos mountains in ancient Armenia. Eventually they settled the whole of the Fertile Crescent of the Mesopotamian plane.[46] When Adam's son Cain murdered his brother Able, Cain was banished by God from the rest of Adam's clan. As a result, Cain "dwelt in the land of Nod on the east of Eden (east of Mesopotamia)."[47] There God put a mark on Cain to protect him from unnamed inhabitants, who already lived in the region. Cain also took a wife from an unnamed population. Later, Genesis 4 says that Cain oversaw the building of a city in Mesopotamia named Eridu, after his son Enoch, who probably had a hand in its establishment.[48,49,50]

This took place about 7000 years ago, as Adam and his descendants were establishing the first civilization on Earth. People in Eridu engaged in commerce with record keeping on cuneiform tablets, marking an enormous advance in human civilization.

Details from Genesis, then, firmly places Adam's clan at the cusp of the age of written history. Likewise, Cain's agrarian lifestyle and Able's animal husbandry are indicative of the end of the neolithic age (stone age). Genesis 4 records that not many generations after Adam, music and the earliest forms of metallurgy were also developed, "He (Jubal) was the father of all those who play the harp and flute. And as for Zillah, she also bore Tubal-Cain, an instructor of every craftsman in bronze and iron."[51]

ADAM'S FALL & A NEW MORAL CODE

Unlike those in the outside world, Adam and Eve had fellowship with God in the Garden of Eden, a paradise. Yet even before the fall, a sinless Adam and Eve were only aware of God when He manifested a presence in the Garden. Genesis 2 says that God Himself planted the Garden, and He placed Adam there to tend it. Even plants in the Garden took some looking after, but this was light work. The garden also contained two very unusual trees, the Tree of Life and the Tree of the Knowledge of Good and Evil. Surely, these two trees were not of this world.

The Tree of Life was probably placed in the garden by God because Adam and Eve were merely human. Such a tree would have made it possible for them to escape the usual cycle of life and death that existed outside the garden.

The tree of the Knowledge of Good and Evil was introduced to the Garden by God as a test. He gave Adam and Eve a single law, if you will. Genesis 2:16-17 says, "And the Lord God commanded the man, saying, "You may surely eat of every tree of the garden, but of the tree of the Knowledge of Good and Evil you shall not eat, for in the day that you eat of it you shall surely die."[52] It is reasonable to believe that Adam had the life experience necessary to understand the concept and possibility of death. In short order, Adam and Eve were tempted by Satan to obtain 'god like' wisdom from this tree, and they disobeyed God by eating from it.

So, Adam and Eve were driven from the mountains of Eden into the outer world, so that they would not eat from the Tree of Life and live forever separated from God. By their unbelief, Adam and Eve exchanged a simple life of light horticulture and fellowship with God for one of toil, constrained by a knowledge of good and evil.

This fall from grace consigned every human being thereafter to be born without knowing God. This state is commonly known as original sin. It is, however, a misconception that rebellion against God originated with Adam and Eve. The serpent who deceived them in the garden, a manifestation of Satan, had already fallen from grace.

Moreover, sin was in the world before Adam. Fischer writes, "a literal interpretation of Romans 5:12-14 indicated the world was populated before Adam. The key was verse 13: "for until the law sin was in the world: but sin is not imputed when there is no law."[53] We know a moral law existed after Adam because sin was imputed to men prior to Moses. The flood as a judgement of sin shows this to be true. Genesis 2 called this law "the knowledge of good and evil." After Adam was expelled from the garden this new moral code was spread to other people, and sin was imputed to human beings outside Eden for the first time.

Paradoxically, in Adam's disobedience God gave mankind a moral code, which is what we now call natural law, or conscience. The new moral code was complex, probably unwritten, and it compelled humanity to rise above the animal kingdom. It was essential for the development of the first civilizations of Mesopotamia. People would never be able to live up to this moral code, but it would make it possible for them to live in the close confines of the first cities, with a degree of harmony. We know that the name of the one true God and Adam's law was spread to others. Genesis 4:26 says that after Seth was born to Adam, "men (in Mesopotamia) began to call upon the name of the Lord."

God Himself added animal sacrifice to the moral code in the Garden, when He provided Adam and Eve with animal skins to cover their nakedness (Genesis 3:21). The law of blood sacrifice for sin reappears in Genesis 4:3-7, with Able and Cain. Able's animal sacrifice followed God's pattern and he was approved by God. Cain's grain sacrifice did not follow the pattern and it was rejected by God. Colossians 2:17 explains that the blood of animals was merely a foreshadow of Christ's sacrifice.

Surprisingly, original sin is also consistent with evolution. Darwin gave us a good secular description of original sin: "There can hardly be a doubt that we are descended from barbarians."[54] One need look no further than this for the universality of sin.

What of the prevalent notion that death entered the created order through Adam's sin? There are two Bible verses outside of Genesis that relate death to Adam's sin. Romans 5:12 says, "Therefore, just as through one man sin entered the world (sin was imputed through Adam's law), and death through sin, and thus death spread to all men, because all sinned."[55] Death spread to all men because all sinned, and not only because of Adam. The other pertinent verse is 1 Corinthians 15:22 which says, "For as in Adam all die, even so in Christ all shall be made alive."[56] This does not mean that all death in the created order was caused by Adam's sin. It means that in Adam as a type, all people are separated from God and die under Adam's law, the knowledge of good and evil. We also know the verse's second "all" does not mean that every human being will have eternal life, but only those who are found in Christ Jesus.

Genesis does not say the world outside Eden changed after Adam's sin, for God rested from creation before the fall. Indeed, no matter where we examine the heavens there has never been a change in the laws of physics. Entropy and random chance, erroneously cited by some as starting with Adam's fall, have always been features of the physics of the universe.

If God used evolution to create all life forms on Earth, and if death is one of the mechanisms of evolution, then tribulation and death were always the lot of life outside the Garden of Eden. This is consistent with the physical evidence that life has existed on Earth for more than 3.5 billion years. Fossils prove that even the earliest animals were designed to eat other living plants and animals. Moreover, Job 38:39, 41 and Psalm 104:21, 25, 27 and Luke 12:24 all say that God Himself provides food for carnivorous animals. Therefore, carnivorous activity related to evolutionary processes cannot be evil in its own right.

Romans 8:20 says, "For the creation was subjected to futility, not willingly, but because of Him who subjected it."[57] This verse is frequently taken to prove that Adam and his sin subjected creation to its current state of death and corruption. But, the One who subjected the universe was God, not Adam. Adam had no power to change the universe. Romans does not say when the universe was subjected to futility, but all the evidence, scientific and biblical, points to the time of creation.

There is a parallel case of sin and expulsion in the Bible. Satan's rebellion arose in Heaven, in a world free of pain and suffering, sometime before Adam's fall on Earth. Possibly, it was Satan's desire to rule the newly created universe that led to his downfall. We can safely assume that the nature of life in heaven was not altered by Satan's rebellion there. Rather he and his angelic followers were cast out of heaven. It follows then that

God would not necessarily alter life on Earth after Adam's rebellion. Adam was simply cast out of Eden's paradise, just as Satan was cast out of Heaven.

A key point of Eden's drama is that, even with every advantage, human beings fall short of God's righteousness. In response to the fall God said, "I will put enmity between you (Satan) and the woman, and between your seed (Satan's) and her Seed (Messiah); He shall bruise your head, and you shall bruise His heel (Genesis 3:15)." God meant that a redeemer would come to crush the serpent and his evil intent for humanity.

Most of the elements of God's curse on Adam and Eve for disobedience came as a matter of course, when they were forced to live in the normal world outside Eden (Genesis 3:14-24). God's curse on Adam climaxes in Genesis 3:19 with a sentence of eventual physical death, "for you are dust, and to dust you shall return."[58] This death sentence was not extended to the rest of the created order, where physical death already existed.

Genesis 5:5 says Adam lived 930 years and then died. The long life spans attributed to Adam and his line may have been the result of the soul life that God had breathed into him. Genesis 6 speaks of two populations, the "sons of God" and the "daughters of men." The Scofield Bible says that, ""the sons of God" refers to all the godly (the line of Adam and Seth), and "daughters of men" refers to all the ungodly, irrespective of their mutual paternity."[59] The mixing of the Adamites and the daughters of the indigenous Mesopotamian population may have attenuated the longevity of the Adamites over time. Alternatively, David Rohl suggests the long life spans of Genesis represent the rein of successive antediluvian patriarchal dynasties, rather than the span of individual lives. I lean toward the view that the early patriarchs actually had long lives.

Actually, there are several clues in the Bible that Eden was never intended to be mankind's permanent home. First, Eden was relatively small geographically. It could not have supported a burgeoning population over time, as the Earth has done. Indeed, there would have been no need for a special garden like Eden if the entire Earth really had been a perfect place without death.

Most importantly, death was always possible for the residents of Eden. The potential for evil was designed into the universe by God from the beginning. Even if Adam and Eve had succeeded in obeying God's command, any future offspring would have also lived under the threat of death for disobedience. By contrast, the Bible says death is not possible in Heaven and that untold millions will be living there. Finally, Revelation 13:8 describes Christ as "the Lamb slain from the foundation of the world." This means it was God's plan from the very beginning that His people would be saved from their sins by Christ, and spend eternity with Him in heaven, rather than in Eden.

Genesis 3:20 makes it clear that, even after the fall, Eve would be the "mother of all living." The essence of the new soul life, that God initially imparted to Adam, persisted in human beings after the fall. So how did the human beings outside Eden become living souls? I think the spark, the communicating soul life that God gave Adam was passed from person to person in much the same way life in Christ is passed on by Christians. It was by personal testimony and by God's Spirit.

It is reasonable to believe that the soul life from God and the new moral code sparked the establishment of human civilization. After Adam and Eve were driven into the outer world, they started sharing their higher way of thinking and communicating with those outside Eden. This was the catalyst for the rapid progression from hunter gatherer troupes, to Mesopotamian cities with written languages.

NOAH'S MESOPOTAMIAN FLOOD

The flood of Genesis, so maligned by skeptics, can also be reconciled with science. To be sure, there are obstacles to overcome. There is not nearly enough water in the world to cover the entire planet, except as a vapor. There is no global sediment layer that would indicate a past planetary flood. Fresh water animals would not have survived a global salt water flood. The long unbroken chains of human lineage in the various parts of the globe (based on DNA) also argue against a global flood.[60] The common belief among Christians that there was no rain prior to the flood is also problematic. But, does the Bible really teach a global flood?

A careful review of the physical evidence and the Bible indicate that Noah's flood was a massive, but localized inundation of Mesopotamia. Mesopotamia is a relatively shallow plain about 300 miles long and 150 miles wide.

There is geological evidence of very heavy flooding at the ancient cities of Ur, Kish, Shuruppak, Uruk and Lavash, more or less simultaneously about 4900 years ago. Fischer substantiates a local flood by the archeology of the Mesopotamian flood deposits, "Analysis of the flood layers at the excavated city sites found only those elements that could be expected from the waters of the Euphrates. No remains of any salt water creatures were present, which indicates none of the flooded cities were inundated by sea water."[61]

But what of the Bible's repeated descriptions of a global flood? Richard Fischer deduces that, "The Bible translators, in the service of King James in the early 1600's, thought at the outset that the Genesis flood was a global event. They were not guided solely by the Hebrew verbiage and syntax, but also by presumptive bias, and fell into the trap of allowing their forgone conclusions to affect the translation."[62]

Fischer and Rich Deem show that the Hebrew word "har", translated in English as "mountains" in the Noah flood account, can be translated as "hills" in every case. In the same vein, the phrase the "whole earth" (*kot eret* in Hebrew) is most frequently used in the Bible metaphorically, or interchangeably with the word "land", or even the "people" of the land. Deem presents a sizable, but abbreviated list of the instances of *kot eret* in scripture referring to specific peoples, or specific locations, and not the entire earth.[63] Fischer rectifies this issue with the appropriate translations of *har* and *kot eret,* in the King James Version of Genesis 1-11.[64]

Other obvious instances of earth not referring to the entire planet include God banishing Cain from Adam's clan. Cain replied, "Behold, this day You have driven me from the face of the earth."[65] Of course, Cain was still on planet Earth when he settled in the land of Nod. Again, during Moses' eighth plague upon Egypt, locusts were so numerous that, "they covered the face of the whole earth."[66] Adjacent Bible verses in Exodus make it clear that the locust covered only the land of Egypt.

2 Peter 3:5-6 also implies the flood was limited to the known world, "by the word of God the heavens existed long ago and the land was formed out of water and by water, through

which *the world at that time* was destroyed, being flooded with water." The known world was in the Mesopotamian plain.

Rich Deem concludes, "There is a word in Hebrew that always refers to the entire earth or the entire inhabited earth. The word is *tebel* (Strong's H8398), which is found 37 times in the Old Testament. Curiously, this word is never used to describe the flood, although it is used extensively to describe the creation of the earth and the judgment of the peoples of the earth."[67]

These facts demonstrate that the Genesis flooding of the "whole earth" should be rendered as the flooding of the "whole land" of Mesopotamia.

THE FLOOD HISTORIES

David Rohl presents a secular argument for the historicity of Noah and a massive Mesopotamian flood. His view is based on Genesis, archeology and contemporary Mesopotamian flood accounts, such as the famous Epic of Gilgamesh.[68]

Other secular accounts corroborate a local flood of Mesopotamian. One reveals Nimrod's motives for building the infamous Tower of Babel. Richard Fischer recounts, "And Nimrod incited them to insolence towards God and contempt. The grandson of Ham, the son of Noah, and a daring man of action, he persuaded them not to attribute to God the prosperity they had through Him, but to think that their own virtue furnished this to them. ... And he started threatening to retaliate against God if He resolved to flood the earth again. For he (Nimrod) would build a tower (tower of Babel) higher than the water was able to reach, and he would avenge the destruction of their forefathers." It was Nimrod's defiance that made this particular Mesopotamian ziggurat an affront to God.[69]

Flavious Josephus, a first century Jewish historian, quoted earlier secular accounts of the flood, "Now all the writers of barbarian histories make mention of this flood, and of this ark; among whom is Berosus the Chaldean. For when he is describing the circumstances of the flood, he goes on thus: "It is said there is still some part of this ship in Armenia, at the mountain of the Cordyaeans; and that some people carry off pieces of the bitumen, which they take away, and use chiefly as amulets for the averting of mischiefs."

Hieronymus the Egyptian also, who wrote the Phoenician Antiquities, and Mnaseas, and a great many more, make mention of the same. Nay, Nicolaus of Damascus, in his ninety-sixth book, hath a particular relation about them; where he speaks thus: "There is a great mountain in Armenia, over Minyas, called Baris, upon which it is reported that many who fled at the time of the Deluge were saved; and that one who was carried in an ark came on shore upon the top of it; and that the remains of the timber were a great while preserved."”[70] These histories testify to Noah's existence, and that some people survived the flood by fleeing to the mountains.

Most believers seem to be unaware that Genesis 6:4 also describes a line of men who survived the flood. They were descended from 'giants' (Nephilim in Hebrew, or fallen ones), "mighty men who were of old, the men of renown." These people lived before the flood, and their descendants were alive centuries after the flood, but they were not Noah's kin. They lived "in what became Canaanite country, the region of Palestine, outside the flood zone."[71]

They were described by the spies that Moses sent to evaluate the promised land of Canaan. Numbers 13:33 is from the spies' report, "And there we saw the Nephilim (the sons of Anak, who come from the Nephilim), and we seemed to ourselves like grasshoppers (*small*), and so we seemed to them." These flood surviving 'giants' are mentioned in Deuteronomy 2:10-11, 2 Samuel 21:15-22, 1 Chronicles 20:6-8 and in Joshua 12:4, 13:12, 15:8, 17:15, and 18:16, to list a few examples.[72] The existence of the post flood descendants of the antediluvian mighty men, is sufficient to prove from the Bible that Noah's flood was regional in scope.

ADAM'S DESCENDANTS JUDGED

Jesus taught that culpability comes with knowledge. He said, "If I had not done among them the works which no one else did, they would have no sin; but now they have seen and also hated both Me and My Father."[73] By this principle, Fischer argues that the flood sent by God was a judgement of the descendants of Adam in Mesopotamia, and not for the destruction of every human being on the Earth.[74] Only the descendants of Adam had the new moral code, or Adam's law, and they alone were held accountable by God.

To support this view, Richard Fischer points to the original Hebrew flood text. It maintains a distinction between the judged Adamites (descendants of Adam) and the rest of mankind. Our Bible translations do not. Fischer preserves the original distinction, between the two groups, by amending the translation of the pertinent words in the King James Version.[75]

Psalm 49:1-2 is another example, ""Hear this all ye people: give ear all ye inhabitants of the world: both low and high, rich and poor, together." The Hebrew phrase *bene 'adam*, translated "low" in the second verse, is literally - "sons of Adam". What comes to us as "high" in this verse is the Hebrew phrase *bene 'ish*. The word *'ish* is a general term meaning "man," "male," "human being," or "mankind." Instead of "low and high," which bears no semblance of meaning from the original Hebrew, either "sons of Adam and sons of man," or "Adamite and Non-Adamite" would have been literal translations, faithful to the Hebrew text.

Ah, but who could the sons of man be who were not sons of Adam? Non-Admaites? How could that be possible? So, translators of the Authorized Version avoided certain controversy by substituting the benign "low and high," virtual synonyms for "poor" and "rich." Modern Bible translations, not having any better ideas, simply followed along."[76]

Centuries later, by Abraham's time, the city of Sodom was the largest and longest reigning city in the plain of the Jordan river. Sodom's location is described in Genesis 13:10, "Lot lifted his eyes (to the east) and saw all the plain of Jordan, that it was well watered everywhere (before the Lord destroyed Sodom and Gomorrah) like the garden of the Lord, like the land of Egypt as you go toward Zoar." This is the plain northeast of the dead sea.

But Sodom had become so wicked, in spite of having Adam's law, that it too was destroyed by God. The destruction of Sodom and Gomorrah has been largely taken as myth by most scientists. But, now the city's remains have been discovered by Dr. Steven Collins at Tall el-Hammam. He has been excavating the city and its palace since 2013.[77] True to the Bible text,

Sodom and the cities of the plain were destroyed by a asteroid or comet airburst with the power of 1000 Hiroshima atomic bombs. Genesis 19:24 says, "the Lord rained brimstone and fire on Sodom and Gomorrah, from the Lord *out of the heavens*."

Mud bricks, the ground, pottery shards and shattered human bones have been uncovered with glassy glazes similar to those found at nuclear test sites. Astrophysicists analyzed these Tall el-Hammam artifacts and found the glazes were indeed caused by extremely high temperatures, resulting from a high energy cosmic airburst.[78]

THE FLOOD WATERS RECEDE

Genesis 8:4 says that the ark came to rest on the mountains (or hills) of Ararat. Ararat, as it is rendered in Hebrew, refers to the mountains or hills of present day Armenia as the ark's resting place.[79] This is not Mount Ararat in Turkey which has been the focus of so many ark finding expeditions.

As the flood waters subsided, Noah sent out a dove that brought an olive leaf back to the ark. This too is indirect evidence of a limited flood. Fisher observes, "Had the entire earth been submerged in salt water for over nine months, plant life would have perished, yet in the mouth of the dove was not a dead olive branch, but a leaf. Could an olive tree survive over nine months underwater: if one did, could it sprout leaves in a week? Or is it more sensible to believe that most of the world, including the region near where the ark landed and the leaf was taken, was spared the flood? ...mention of an olive leaf in Genesis 8:11 supports a local flood and negates a global flood."[80]

Rich Deem considers the altitude of the ark's resting place, "If the ark had come to rest on the top of Mount Ararat, this would be at 17,000 foot elevation. Olive trees (and every other tree) do not grow at 17,000 feet. In fact, you will not find olive trees growing much above 5,000 feet. Therefore, we know from the Bible that the ark did not come to rest on, or near the top of Mount Ararat, but probably somewhere on the foothills."[81] It is also unlikely that Noah's clan, animals in tow, could have descended from 17,000 feet without climbing gear, or the modern convenience of oxygen.

Deem continues, "The method by which the flood ended also tells us that the flood was local. According to Genesis, the water receded and was dried by the wind. If the flood were global, there would be no place for the waters to recede to. Likewise, a wind would not significantly affect a global flood."[81]

Finally, a local flood is inferred from the verses describing the drying of the waters. Genesis 8:6-7 says, "(Noah) sent forth a raven. It went to and fro until the waters were dried up from the earth." Genesis 8:13 similarly states, "the water was dried up from the earth," and in Genesis 8:14, "the earth was completely dry." Rich Deem quips, "If one were to interpret these verses from a global perspective, one would have to conclude that the entire earth became a desert after the flood."[81] Clearly, the translation should indicate that the local flood zone was dry, and not the entire planet.

In view of all these facts from Genesis, science and history, the logical interpretation of Noah's flood is that it was a massive flood of Mesopotamian cities. The Bible's original text has not been changed in any way by this.

RAIN, RIBS & DINOSAURS

As to the issue of the first rain, the Bible does not say it never rained before Noah's flood. Genesis 2: 4-6 does say, "This is the history of the heavens and the earth when they were created, in the day that the LORD God made the earth and the heavens, before any plant of the field was in the earth and before any herb of the field had grown. For the LORD God had not caused it to rain on the earth, and there was no man to till the ground; but a mist went up from the earth and watered the whole face of the ground."[82]

The time when there was no rain is described as "before man, or trees of the field," and the absence of rain is given as the reason that there were no large plants. Trees and mankind were present at the time of Noah—he used trees to make his ark. So Genesis actually implies that rain had already occurred long before Noah's time, which is consistent with science. Noah's Mesopotamian flood resulted from an enormous amount of rain and water from the fountains of the Earth, which probably included melting glaciers in the north.

There is even an indirect assent to the theory of evolution in the flood story. In Genesis 6:7 "the LORD said, "I will blot out man whom I have created from the face of the land, man and animals and creeping things and birds of the heavens, for I am sorry that I have made them.""[83] God was sorry He had created Adam's descendants, because of their extraordinarily violent and evil ways. Yet, why would God regret making animals? It is probably that mankind's lower nature had its origin in the animals.

Some of the stranger sounding details of the creation of Adam and Eve can also be seen as consistent with science. God removed one of Adam's ribs to fashion Eve, in Genesis 2:21-23, "So the LORD God caused a deep sleep to fall upon the man, and while He slept took one of his ribs and closed up its place with flesh. And the rib that the LORD God had taken from the man He made into a woman and brought her to the man."[84] Now here is an amazing fact: chimpanzees have thirteen rib sets, and humans generally have only twelve.[85] The Genesis 2 passage seems to reflect a physical difference between humans and our pre-hominid ancestors, chimpanzees. Might it be that Adam's deep sleep, and the creation of Eve from his rib is a metaphor for the transition from pre humans to homo sapiens?

Many other details of the Bible have been reconciled with science in lucid fashion by authors like Hugh Ross, Francis Collins, Gerald Schroeder, David Rohl and Richard Fischer. Schroeder even finds mention of dinosaurs hidden in Old Testament scripture. He deftly compares Genesis 1:21 and Exodus 7:10,15 to interpret the phrase *taninim gedolim* to mean "the big reptiles", or dinosaurs.[86] He has also identified the small transitional animal archaeopteryx, part reptile and part bird, in Leviticus 11:18, 30 by the name *tinshemet.*[87]

A Divine source of knowledge for Genesis is borne out by all of these truths.

DESIGN IS REAL

Atheists pin their hope against God in the undirected nature of random events in evolution. But even these random events are driven and constrained by physical laws, and those laws are identically the same as design. The constants of those laws had to be tuned with extreme precision for a universe to exist, that could support life. Design is not negated by tiny random occurrences, as atheists claim, but is based on the bedrock of the physical laws for which the materialists have no proven explanation. Moreover, atheists misconstrue the theological ramifications of random events, as we will see in the chapter on the uncertainty principle.

Antony Flew, former atheist and philosopher, holds to the reality of design: "Although I was once sharply critical of the argument of design, I have since come to see that, when correctly formulated, this argument constitutes a persuasive case for the existence of God. Developments in two areas, in particular, have led me to this conclusion. The first is the question of the origin of the laws of nature and the related insights of eminent modern scientists. The second is the question of the origin of life and reproduction."[88] Belief in Divine design is reasonable and it does not rest on gaps in our scientific knowledge, but in the philosophical conundrum of origins, which the equations of science cannot explain.

PLANETARY EVOLUTION

Planet Earth also evolves. Its evolution is driven largely by its molten core, which is heated by radioactive materials deep inside the planet, and by the Sun's energy. The liquid upper portion of the Earth's core produces an electric current as the Earth rotates, and this generates a large magnetic field around our planet—the magnetosphere. The Earth's magnetosphere diverts cosmic rays and solar flares, protecting our upper atmosphere and preventing it from "boiling" away. Beneath the Earth's surface, the molten mantle causes the outer crust, or solid land, to move in a process called plate tectonics. This same process also produces earthquakes, and volcanoes of hot lava that vent up from the molten mantle through the Earth's crust.[89]

Most of the rocky planetary bodies in the solar system display large numbers of meteor impacts, with craters lying on top of other craters, except on Earth. Here the surface has been plowed, crushed and overflowed by water, wind, tectonic plate movement and volcanism. In fact, most of Earth's impact craters are so eroded and buried, only the largest ones can be seen from space.

Collisions of the major land mass plates created our majestic mountains. Spewing volcanoes brought minerals and water up from deep within the planet, making Earth habitable. As destructive as earthquakes and volcanoes can be, there is just enough geological activity to sustain the planetary magnetic field that protects us and the atmosphere from space radiation. Yet there is not so much activity that ecologies and societies are completely disrupted.

Without the internal geological forces that drive the occasional earthquake, volcano and tsunami, the Earth would cool, lose most of its atmosphere and its ability to support complex life. Earth would soon become a dead planet much like Mars. These massive planetary forces seemed to have been balanced by the loving hand of the Creator, to create a generally benevolent Earth.

There are many other features of the Earth that are tuned for life, such as an abundance of heavy elements from which life forms are made. Earth has a right-sized gravity, and the necessary atmospheric oxygen concentration to foster large biological life forms. These complex large-bodied animals appeared on Earth at virtually the same time the atmospheric oxygen concentration became high enough to support their metabolism.[90] No scientist knows how they arose so quickly after conditions were favorable.

The Copernican principle says that our little part of the universe is not intrinsically different from any other part of the universe. Yet we know for sure that we dwell on a privileged planet, the only known island of sentience and free will. The next locale in the universe that might harbor intelligent beings similar to us is many light years away at the very least. This is why God charged Adam and Eve, and later Noah, to "replenish the Earth," in the words of the older King James Bible. Therefore, the Bible can hardly be blamed for ecological damage to the Earth.[91]

From the parched barren surface of Mercury to the hellish acidic atmosphere of Venus, the Earth stands out as a miracle world. The odds against the existence of another world nearby as wonderful as Earth are imposing.[92] It took a galaxy of mind-boggling scale to produce a planet with just the right orbit, with a stabilizing moon, just the right size and the right atmosphere, along with liquid water to support large complex life forms. I believe it is legitimate to see the conditions on Earth as a proof mark of God.

Atheists would say that in a universe so large, the Earth is just a happy accident. But if you know in your innermost being that God exists, it does not take much faith to see His hand in our existence. I believe it is reasonable to take the consistency of the Bible with cosmology and evolutionary science as an extraordinary sign of God's supernatural revelation. Nothing from science needs to be a stumbling block to faith in Christ.

CHAPTER FOUR

TO THE MOON & MARS

"Everything belongs to the Lord your God, not only the earth and everything on it, but also the sky and the highest heavens."
~ Deuteronomy 10:14 Contemporary English Version (CEV)

During my childhood, traveling to the Moon was just a dream. I was only six years old in October 1957 when Sputnik was launched by the Soviet Union. It was the first artificial satellite in Earth orbit. One evening a neighbor pointed out Sputnik to me as a slow moving star in the dark night sky of my small hometown. I was amazed that I was able to see a real space satellite with my own eyes, (actually, the larger rocket booster) and that my neighbor knew how to locate it.

Even at my age I was aware of the angst caused in America by Sputnik. The ability to launch satellites into Earth orbit meant the Russians could also launch nuclear bombs to any point in America. But I did not realize that I was witnessing the beginning of the age of planetary exploration, or that space systems engineering would be in my future.

On Easter of 1962, my first small aerospace adventure was set into motion. My parents took me to the city's Easter egg hunt, where notes with different prizes were taped to brightly colored candy eggs. I ran ahead of the other kids, picking up eggs as I went. I rejected the first couple of eggs I found, ran a few more feet and picked up one last egg. I read its label, "Flight in Murray Inman's Airplane," and quickly shoved the egg into my pocket. I could hardly believe my eyes. Murray Inman's Beechcraft was the nicest airplane in my hometown, and I would have an airplane ride! Having my dad on the twenty minute flight gave me confidence to go.

We flew skyward on a fine spring day with scattered billowing clouds and great visibility, and as we stopped climbing Mr. Inman announced, "We're at 6000 feet!" I looked out the window at the flat farmlands below and remarked, "I've been higher than this in a car." That was on a family vacation that took us through the mountains. But I was not unimpressed with my flight. This was just my low key manner of speaking. I was thankful that, of all the kids in Hartford City, I got to fly. It was something I would not otherwise have been able to do. This experience fueled my growing interest in all things aviation. Of course, my mother made sure I wrote a letter of thanks to Mr. Inman.

In 1961 President Kennedy committed America to land astronauts on the Moon, with the aim of beating the Russians there. The following May, in a prelude to the Moon landings, astronaut Alan Shepard sat in a Mercury capsule, atop a Redstone rocket at Cape Canaveral. He was ready to attempt America's first man into space. Back in Indiana, the teachers at my school ushered us into the gymnasium to watch Shepard's sub orbital flight on television. We didn't know what to expect, but it was all very exciting. We were aware of the large number of US rocket failures that had occurred in the build up to this launch. We were not aware that the Redstone Rocket that Shepard was on was America's most reliable large rocket. It was a converted Army ballistic missile designed by rocket scientist Werner Von Braun.

It was a little deflating that the Russians had put Yuri Gagarin into earth orbit just three weeks before, and that our first manned mission would only have a short suborbital trajectory. Even so, our hearts raced as we anticipated Shepard's hurtle into space. On lift off his rocket quickly exceeded the range of the television cameras, and we could only imagine what was happening as his flight progressed. We listened to him relay flight information, and after a short time, newscaster Walter Cronkite declared Shepard's successful water landing. Everyone was so excited! Eventually, in 1971 Alan Shepard would be one of twelve men to walk on the Moon and return safely to Earth.

Each time a US space launch was planned during school hours we were allowed to watch it on television. It was great fun to get out of class, but it was more exciting to see Americans fly into space. It impressed me that America was open enough to broadcast each launch live. The Russian communists only announced successful launches, and only after their cosmonauts were safely on the ground. Failures and deaths were never announced. It felt good to know that our teachers thought enough of us to let us witness history in the making. The whole thing made me proud to be an American.

By Christmas Eve 1968, the Apollo 8 astronauts circumnavigated the Moon for the first time. We rushed home from a Christmas Eve service to turn on the television to watch the first ever live broadcast from lunar orbit. To my amazement the astronauts read from the Genesis 1 creation story to mark the occasion.

As I watched, I had a palpable sense of God's presence, and felt a close connection with the astronauts reading from scripture, a quarter of a million miles away. To my mind there has never been a more sublime moment in man's effort to explore space. Sadly, I doubt that astronauts today would be permitted such a public expression of personal Christian faith. Only the Apollo 11 moon landing on live television was as engaging. By the end of 1972, a dozen Americans had landed on the moon in seven missions, culminating one of the greatest technical feats of all time.

In my estimation, the campaign to land on, and explore the Moon was one of the most noble and exhilarating endeavors mankind has ever undertaken, even though it started as a technology race with the Russians. By the time of the Moon landings, the Russians were conspicuous by their absence, and the US moon missions looked downright altruistic.

This singular achievement inspired young people like myself to dreams of space flight, and an education in science and engineering. But getting there was not easy for me. In Junior High school, my class had to take a mathematics proficiency test that would determine who would go on to algebra. I was so bored and behind in math by that time, I missed the cutoff for algebra class by one point. My father had convinced me that most jet pilots were engineers, and the only way I could be a pilot, or work on aircraft was to study algebra. To my great relief, I persuaded my guidance counselor Mr. Landis to let me enroll in algebra, but it took a whole year to catch up with the rest of the class. Still, I could sense that I was on my way to an exciting future.

OUR UNIQUE MOON

The Moon multiplies the Earth's good fortune. In ages past the Moon has taken many major asteroid and comet impacts in our stead, as evidenced by its scarred surface.

The Moon has just the right mass to stabilize the tilt of the Earth.[1] It is the Earth's tilt that creates the four seasons, thereby preventing runaway heating. Moreover, if the Earth's rotation were not stabilized by the gravitational tug of the Moon, there would be more frequent climate changes. The mean time between ice ages might be so short as to blunt the development of human societies. Ocean tides generated by the Moon also helped establish the biological rhythms for many organisms on the Earth.

The Moon gives our species a permanent view of a planetary body, providing a tangible way to see the true nature of the Earth and other planets. In a fortuitous example of fine tuning in nature, the Moon is the same apparent size as the Sun for an observer on the Earth. This produces solar and lunar eclipses, which heightened early man's inquisitiveness about space. This even made it possible to perform direct observations of the Sun's corona before modern instruments were developed. I think it is reasonable, then, to believe in Divine fine tuning of the Earth-Moon configuration.

We still don't know exactly how the Moon was formed. It may have been created at the same time as Earth, from the same disk of dust around the Sun, or it may be the result of an ancient and massive planetary collision with a proto- earth. Both scenarios have unresolved issues.[2] In any event, the Moon is now tidally locked with the Earth meaning that the same side of the Moon always faces the Earth.

The Moon was long thought to be bone dry, but millions of tons of water ice have been discovered in the perpetual shadows of several craters at the lunar south pole. The Clementine spacecraft, and the Lunar Prospector made this surprise discovery. The presence of water was then confirmed using a NASA radar aboard India's Chandrayaan- I lunar orbiter, and by the Lunar Crater Observation and Sensing Satellite (LCROSS).[3]

The presence of water means that it may be easier for humans to explore and inhabit the Moon than has been generally supposed. There are even plans by private companies, like Moon Express, to mine precious metals and exotic elements from the Moon's surface. Clearly, the Moon has been a good partner to our home world. It is a source of Divine blessings, fulfilling the Psalm that calls the Moon, "the faithful witness of the sky."[4]

THE RED PLANET

Mars has long been an object of fascination. It is the next planet at 140 million miles from the Sun, and the last terrestrial planet in our system, except for the extremely distant dwarf planets Ceres and Pluto. Mars is the most familiar of all the planets in the solar system, having an atmosphere, mountains, plains, canyons created by water flows, and polar caps of water and carbon dioxide ice.

As a kid, I was excited about the possibility of water canals and intelligent beings on Mars. At the turn of the 20th century, American astronomer Percival Lowell had popularized the idea that Martian canals were observable from Earth, and that these were evidence of advanced intelligent life on Mars. Detailed maps of the canal system were even published.[5] Television programs about the Martians and their expansive canals peaked my imagination, but at the same time serious scientists were claiming that the Martian canals were mere optical illusions.

As a teenager in 1965, I could not let go of the idea of canals and a Martian civilization, until images from the Mariner 4 spacecraft finally revealed a dry barren Mars. It was more like the moon than a habitable world.[6] I still remember my acute disappointment with the images of the parched planet, with no canals, and definitely no Martians. The scientists who said there were no canals were proven correct.

Let me hasten to add that I have since learned to appreciate Mars just as it is: a fascinating solar system partner. From Mars we are learning a great deal about planetary evolution, climate, and conditions that may or may not support life.

THE UNFORGIVING ENTERPRISE OF SPACE

My first involvement with a mission to Mars was the Mars Observer project. Missions to Mars from all countries have had an unusually high failure rate. More than fifty percent of all missions to Mars have failed. Mars Observer was a complex 500 million dollar science mission, which was designed to orbit Mars with a suite of sensitive science instruments. Mars Observer was intended to monitor the Martian climate, photograph its surface in high resolution, and create accurate laser rangefinder topographical maps of the planet. Over the next nine years Mars Observer would become the central project of my career, and my first experience as a lead engineer on a spacecraft project.

I monitored the progress of the spacecraft contractor GE Aerospace. This involved frequent trips to Princeton New Jersey, which lasted three days or more. There were numerous instrument and assembly vibration tests throughout the program. With three little ones at home my wife and I were both a bit sleep deprived. My wife missed me when I was away, but she understood my job's travel requirements. I took her along on trips when her parents could watch the kids.

Back at JPL, a few days after my third daughter's birth, one of the group supervisors brought a small TV to work. Several of my work mates gathered around enthusiastically to watch the Space Shuttle Challenger launch. This mission was taking a teacher into space, a first. I had analyzed Space Shuttle acoustic and vibration data from earlier flights, so the launch was uniquely engaging for me.

We watched as the three Shuttle orbiter main engines ignited and quickly increased thrust to full power. The force of a million pounds of thrust bent the whole launch vehicle against its solid rocket launch locks. As the massive system sprang back to vertical, the two solid rocket boosters were ignited, the launch locks were released and the huge space vehicle began heading skyward. It cleared the launch tower and quickly gathered speed.

No one was aware at the time, but the solid rocket booster on the right side of the orbiter immediately sprang a leak of hot gas through its casing seals, near the base of the Shuttle's main external fuel tank. A heavy wind gust blew the massive Space

Shuttle sideways, momentarily creating a kink in its growing rocket plume. The Shuttle shrugged off the insult and continued its climb. But within the flight's first minute the solid rocket gas leak had become a blowtorch that began cutting through the external fuel tank and its support brackets.

Seventy three seconds into the flight, pilot Michael Smith was heard to say, "Uh, oh..." Half a second later the main fuel tank erupted into a huge fireball, consuming the entire vehicle. Space Shuttle Challenger was gone, along with its crew of seven souls. Smoking chunks and fragments rained down into the Atlantic Ocean, as the two large solid rocket boosters flew on eerily. Later, it was discovered that at least some of the seven astronauts were still alive until the crew cabin crashed into the ocean's surface.

It was a terrible blow. My friend George and I could do nothing the rest of the day, but watch replays of the disaster. I took a long aimless walk, consumed by what I had just witnessed. Everyone at the laboratory was stunned. It was an unprecedented setback for the manned space program, and for the JPL projects that were scheduled to fly into space on the Space Shuttle. The orbiter would not fly again for 32 long months. The delays for the Hubble Space Telescope, and the Galileo spacecraft to Jupiter, would be much longer.

The Challenger explosion revealed just how unforgiving the enterprise of space can be. A management decision to launch outside Shuttle launch parameters, on an abnormally cold day had precipitated disaster. America had never lost people in space, but now seven astronauts were dead, and the multi billion dollar orbiter program was paused. It seemed that nature enjoyed exploiting any possible weaknesses in space hardware to terrible effect, no matter how seemingly obscure. This time it was a stiff 'O' ring seal on a cold Florida morning. The cold seals allowed super heated rocket exhaust to breach the solid rocket case, in just the location that would burn through the Shuttle main fuel tank, igniting a cataclysmic inferno.

Over the next several months, in a somber mood, NASA engineers struggled to understand what had gone so wrong and how to fix it. Most haunting of all was the quest to prevent a future Space Shuttle calamity, but what seemingly benign issue might lead to the next catastrophe? That was the grim question that defied a satisfactory answer. In space travel there are very few benign problems.

It was on the Mars Observer project, a few months later, that I made the biggest blunder of my career. We were testing a radiator for the PMIRR instrument (Pressure Modulator Infrared Radiometer) at a contractor's facility. Unfortunately, the contractor tested the cooler to an old vibration specification that was too high. A heavy copper element inside failed, causing a great deal of internal damage. I missed the contractor's error, which was a huge embarrassment for me. A failure review was convened at which I presented the facts of the case and my job was on the line. However, I was given grace in a most Christian way. The Mars Observer project kept me on, believing I would learn from my mistake. I was left with a painful battle scar that taught me to double check my perceptions, and to be more assertive in checking test parameters. I never made the same mistake again.

The failed part was redesigned. It turned out that its copper material was only one tenth as strong as advertised, and it would not have survived a vibration test to the correct level. The radiator was rebuilt and retested using a new vibration test method that limited test forces as well as acceleration, a first on JPL flight hardware. This gave me a chance to work directly with our top engineer Terry Scharton. The redesigned radiator passed its modified vibration test, but I had a hard time putting the failure of the first test behind me.

I carried on testing instruments and supporting the spacecraft test planning, doing the best I knew how. Finally, the Mars Observer spacecraft was vibration tested on a large shaker at GE, in Princeton New Jersey. A test shaker is like a large speaker element that produces a specified vibration spectrum. I was captivated watching the antenna and solar array oscillating during the system vibration test.

A vibration test on a shaker can sound just like a rocket launch, but not nearly as loud. In some cases it is loud enough to require hearing protection. Even so, engineers typically stand next to a shaker during a vibration test to watch their hardware with their finger on a 'chicken' switch, ready to shut down the test if something looks amiss.

A great deal of preparation is required to get ready for a vibration test. Fixtures have to be made, accelerometers installed on hardware, force transducers mounted and shaker systems verified. Then the flight hardware is mounted and we proceed with the test. A test begins with vibration much lower than the actual test requirement to re-verify the shaker control, test responses, and any limits on vibration levels. Only then did we perform the full level test on MO.

Finally, MO was installed in an acoustic chamber to blast it with high intensity noise to prove it for flight. Because of the test margins, an acoustic noise test is louder than the rocket noise inside a rocket payload fairing. No one can be inside the massive concrete acoustic chamber while the test is going on, if you want to stay alive that is. The sound alone could kill you, and the nitrogen gas that powers the noise generating horns is an asphyxiation risk. During an acoustic test, nitrogen blown through the noise generating horns gradually replaces the oxygen in the acoustic chamber. As the test wears on, the air inside will no longer support life. Space engineers have actually been killed due to nitrogen asphyxiation. One engineer died inside a Space Shuttle engine compartment due to a nitrogen leak.

The Mars Observer spacecraft pyro firing tests were also exciting. You could hear the bang of the pyro initiators and watch a payload adapter ring fall away to padding on the floor. Similarly, the solar panel restraint cables went streaking across the floor as tie down cable cutters were fired. Then the spacecraft was thermal vacuum tested to simulate the environment of space. After this, the spacecraft was made ready for flight.

As a project finale, my family traveled to Cocoa Beach Florida in 1992 to witness the Mars Observer (MO) launch. We met Calvin Harr, my college roommate, and his family there. We gathered on a Cape Canaveral causeway with a large up beat crowd, to watch a massive Titan III rocket send MO on a trajectory to Mars.

As the rocket lit up, I started juggling cameras excitedly to take photos and a movie of its ascent. Suddenly, my knees almost buckled as I watched the rocket rise. The thought came over me that maybe I had missed something that would cause the whole mission to fail. I uttered a brief prayer for God's help and success.

The launch went without a hitch and MO was on a picture perfect course for Mars. Then, eerily, after 9 months in transit, communication with the spacecraft was lost just as it was programed to fire its braking thrusters to enter Mars orbit. Nearly a decade of my career and more than 500 million dollars were lost. It was a real blow to the midsection.

The failure occurred during a pyrotechnic opening of a fuel valve, creating a shock event. Shock testing hardware for Mars Observer had been my responsibility, and I felt sure that the valve shock event had damaged some untested electronics. A suicidal doom pressed in on me and I thought that everyone at the laboratory would know that the mission's loss was my fault. No one actually suggested this, but the lingering humiliation of the cooler test debacle heightened my vulnerability to self recrimination.

Still, I could not imagine what might have been missed in the spacecraft test program; all the pyro devices had been test fired in the system before the flight. Thankfully, God's grace preserved me in those first days after the loss of Mars Observer.

During an agonizing months long failure review, it became obvious that the mission's loss could not have been caused by a deficiency in my work. I was relieved, but still smarting. The loss took a toll on the entire laboratory. In response, the lab director Ed Stone addressed the laboratory in the closest thing to a requiem that I can remember at JPL. His bearing and his remarks comforted me at a time I really needed solace.

The likely cause of failure was a leaky fuel valve that seeped fuel improperly into a propulsion supply tube. The fuel valves were adapted from an Earth orbiting spacecraft design and were not intended to remain dormant for the months long journey to Mars. When the pyro valves were fired to provide fuel and pressure to the main rocket engine, the two hypergolic fuel components met in the fuel line, where the leak had occurred.

Hypergolic fuel comprises two separate components that ignite spontaneously when mixed, so when the two fuel components met in the fuel line and ignited, the small tube ruptured. Pressure in the fuel tanks forced fuel out of the blown line and this momentum started spinning the spacecraft, so that it could not regain a stable attitude. Most likely MO still orbits the Sun as a dead spinning hulk.

The complete and sudden failure of Mars Observer, after so many procedure reviews and careful analyses, and after a multitude of spacecraft assembly and subsystem tests, shook my faith in the engineering process. It became apparent that success was not assured no matter how much care was meant for the process. One small mistake, or oversight, could bring down an entire mission. I reminded myself that I was not to blame for the mission loss and I allowed myself to grieve.

How does one get over a total mission loss? How do you recover self esteem after a glaring test mistake? At some level I realized that it was the journey, and not the destination that is important. I knew that JPL's great legacy had been built one mission at a time, with each team member striving to excel each day. Yes, I grieved, but instead of dwelling on the past, I assimilated life's lessons and moved forward. Mars Observer had not been the space program's first failure, nor would it be the last. Still, I was a changed man.

Even though JPL had many more successes to its credit than failures, NASA circulated talk of shutting JPL down. Could NASA really believe that another large JPL space mission wasn't worth the risk of time and treasure? The threat to shut us down never materialized, though the MO spacecraft contractor GE was shut down permanently. History would show that the principal effect of this move would not improve space mission reliability or reduce costs, but it would permanently narrow the government's choice of spacecraft contractors.

All of us at JPL were required to take a Total Quality Management class, which emphasized documenting processes and customer focus. Oddly enough, a famous fast food hamburger restaurant was held up as a prime example of how to establish and follow procedures. This annoyed me since a "one of a kind" spacecraft is nothing like an average production line hamburger. We took our lumps and soldiered on with the hazardous business of space exploration.

ON MARS!

For rocket scientists success at Mars is its own reward. It has some of the most spectacular topography in the entire solar system, including the highest mountain, Olympus Mons. It is 13 miles high (almost 69,000 feet) owing to the low Martian gravity and slow erosion rates, as compared to Earth. The most massive and longest canyon in the solar system is also on Mars, the Canyon Valles Marineris. It stretches 2700 miles—it would span the United States—and it is up to 4.7 miles deep. As on Earth, the Martian canyon was created by the flow of liquid water millions of years ago, and possibly aided by a rupture of the surface as the planet's interior cooled.

Mars, at 11% of Earth's mass, is not massive enough to maintain a sizable molten core to the present day. Therefore, much of its internal heat has radiated into space, a process that takes millions of years. First, Mars lost its magnetosphere as its core cooled and solidified; and then the solar winds reduced a large portion of its atmosphere into space. Most of the rest of the Martian atmosphere has been frozen into the soil, along with the Martian water. What remains of the Martian atmosphere today is only one thousandth as thick as Earth's atmosphere and, alas, it is a poisonous mixture of 95% carbon dioxide with nitrogen. This is very similar to Venus's deadly atmosphere, so the Earth is shown again to be a miraculous planet.

In 1976 the Mars Viking Landers gave us our first on-the-surface view of the red planet, followed by the Mars rovers Pathfinder, Spirit and Opportunity. Then, in 2008, the Phoenix Mars Lander touched down on Mars, handling and analyzing readily accessible water ice in the Martian soil.[7]

What water Mars still has, and it seems to have a lot, is frozen in the top layer of its soil and at the planet's poles. Incredibly, there are still occasional brief flows of liquid water on Mars. New gullies down the slopes of crater walls have been found in surface images.[8] There are even subterranean water ice glaciers on Mars that have plowed through large crater walls.

Because of its thin atmosphere and its distance from the Sun, Mars is very cold (it gets down to –87°C). Yet, the solar radiation on the surface is so intense that only the most extreme bacterial life forms could survive there. Even so, Martian water means life is possible for indigenous life forms, or for humans visiting from Earth. Recent experiments duplicating Martian radiation and soil confirm that it is technically possible for some hardy types of bacteria to live in the Martian regions that contain subterranean water.[9]

In 2009 NASA announced that methane was present on Mars, creating a huge stir.[10] Methane is a signature of life—a gaseous waste product—and there seems to be a lot of methane on Mars. The annual methane bloom was estimated at 19,000 metric tons every Martian summer. In September 2013 in a dramatic reversal, NASA said that the newest Mars surface rover Curiosity failed to detect methane at any level of concentration. Then move forward to December 2014. NASA announced that Curiosity had detected an increase in methane after all, and theories for its creation were elaborated.[11]

Methane can be produced by volcanic activity, but no such activity is known on Mars currently. The most exciting possibility is methane produced by Martian life, in the water soaked soil. This would not be a bunch of wiggling Martian worms or bugs, but masses of tiny microbes, if they exist. Methane might also be released from a clathrate, a compound that could store methane in the Martian soil. In this case the question still remains about how the methane got into the clathrates in the first place. One day I am sure we will find the source of the methane.

Details of a watery past in the Martian terrain have been cataloged in great detail by surface rovers, and from above by orbiting spacecraft. Spirit and Opportunity are wheeled vehicles on Mars, about the size of a golf cart. They were designed to roam Mars and perform geological science for 90 Martian days, but they far exceeded their mission goals.[12]

Spirit and Opportunity braved rock hazards, sand pits and steep crater walls to be our virtual presence on Mars. Navigation engineers uploaded new driving and science instructions to the pair of rovers daily. Then the rovers would maneuver themselves autonomously, more than 35 million miles from Earth.

Rover Spirit eventually got stuck in sand in 2009. Engineers labored mightily to free Spirit from the sand, testing driving techniques with a twin Earth bound rover in a simulated Martian sand pit, but to no avail. Immobilized, Spirit was no longer able to optimize the position of its solar arrays, its batteries gave out and it did not survive the ensuing Martian winter.

Its twin Rover Opportunity kept on for 15 years, driving more than 28 miles across the lonely Martian surface, taking geological and weather data along the way.[13]

A new larger rover Curiosity is now exploring the Martian surface in unprecedented detail. Its mission is to study the geology, chemistry and radiation on the Martian surface. Rover Curiosity is about the size of a small car, and it has a Radio Thermal Generator, a radioactive heat source for generating electricity. This power source has enabled Curiosity to go where solar powered rovers cannot go, to follow signs of water and look for evidence of Martian life, past or present.

I was privileged to co-direct the vibration test of this magnificent machine with my colleague and friend Juan Fernandez. The rover had a price tag of more than 2 billion dollars, so this was no small thing. The vibration test of the Curiosity rover was performed using a large test shaker. In attendance were representatives from NASA Goddard and from CNES of France. These were organizations that provided instruments for the rover. The vibration test was intended to simulate the shaking that Curiosity would encounter during its rocket launch to Mars, and during its descent and landing.

The visiting teams had to be convinced, along with our own stress engineers, that the vibration responses being measured were not a threat to any Rover hardware. Agreeing on this, we completed the system vibration test without additional test constraints, and without any hardware anomalies. The rover was soon readied for launch.

Rover Curiosity has already discovered that sufficient conditions existed in the distant past to support rudimentary life forms.[14] Curiosity now has a sibling, rover Perseverance, which is drilling core samples of Martian rock for later delivery to Earth. Perseverance also delivered the first helicopter to Mars, and it has taken several successful flights.

Indeed, the images and science data from our growing fleet of robot explorers has been nothing short of spectacular. The most recent images from Mars look so familiar you can imagine walking its barren deserts in search of water and alien life forms. Some day, a youngster reading this book may do that very thing.

There are places you can go in the United States that look very like an alien world. The landscape of Hawaii Volcanoes National Park, for example, is a vast barren undulating mass of volcanic rock, hot steam vents, lava tunnels, and ledges. My daughter and I nearly burned our hands foolishly testing the temperature of the steam vents. The rocky landscape is so expansive that it calls to mind Astronaut Buzz Aldrin's description of the Moon, "A magnificent desolation."

For now Mars exploration is being carried out by our faithful unmanned robotic representatives like the Mars Global Surveyor, the Mars Reconnaissance Orbiter, and the Curiosity rover.

One day, one of our robot explorers will likely give us a definitive answer as to whether life exists on Mars, or if it ever did. Any form of Martian life, past or present, would be consistent with the Genesis command that "earth", in the generic sense, should bring forth life. Either way, it is clear that surviving on Mars would be a tough challenge for a team of astronauts, even with the most sophisticated equipment and provisions, in great contrast to living on Earth.

Next, let us look to the outer solar system to see just how different planets and moons can be.

CHAPTER FIVE

TERRORS & GREAT SIGNS

"There will be signs in the sun and moon and stars, and on the earth there will be dismay among the nations and bewilderment at the roar of the surging sea. Men's courage will fail completely as they realize what is threatening the world, for the very powers of heaven will be shaken"
~ Luke 21:25-26, J.B. Phillips New Testament.

Jesus said great signs would precede His return to Earth one day and that among them would be, "terrors and great signs from heaven."[1] Atheists say the terrors and great signs of the Bible are the things of myth and superstition, but the science of these signs is real enough. Astronomy has recorded so many great signs from the heavens that scientists don't have the resources to study all the data. I believe the unprecedented feat of men standing on the Moon, scientific discoveries at Mars, and the terrors that we face today, both man-made and natural, are sufficient to fulfill Jesus' prophecy of terrors and signs.

So what are the great signs of the outer solar system? Some of the most stunning and potentially deadly heavenly wonders have been discovered beyond Mars by the JPL spacecraft Voyager, Galileo and Cassini. This is the realm of giant gas planets and planetary debris that never coalesced to form bodies larger than asteroids and comets. It is a wholly foreign and desolate cold region of space, with planets aptly named after Greek gods and devils, too far from the Sun and far too cold to support life as we know it.

Imagine a planet made almost entirely of hydrogen gas, the lightest element, yet it comprises 318 Earth masses. Jupiter is so large that 1300 Earths would fit inside its perimeter. Jupiter's less large gassy siblings include Saturn, Uranus and Neptune. Each of these gas giant planets is progressively more distant from the Sun, and each one is much larger than the Earth.

Jupiter's atmosphere of turbulent, colorful, jet stream cloud layers include the largest and oldest known storm cell in the solar system, the Great Red Spot. Galileo was the first person to spy the great red storm 400 years ago with his telescope and it is still raging. Like all giant gas planets, Jupiter has a small rocky core. Atmospheric pressures near the planet's core are astronomical; any spacecraft would be crushed long before reaching landfall. Even so, planet Jupiter would need 75 times more mass to compress its hydrogen fuel enough to ignite a nuclear fusion reaction, and become a new star.

Jupiter is about five times farther from the Sun than the Earth, and, surprisingly, it emits more heat than it receives from the Sun. Most of Jupiter's heat is generated internally by the contraction of its hydrogen gas, under the force of its own gravity. This means gigantic Jupiter is continually getting smaller.

In 1610 Galileo discovered Jupiter's four largest moons: Io, Europa, Ganymede and Callisto. Hence, they are called the Galilean moons, all of them bright enough to be seen from Earth with binoculars. In the modern era, Jupiter has been reconnoitered by the Voyager 1 and 2 spacecraft, and by spacecraft Galileo.

I was at Rockwell's B-1 division when the first flyby images of Jupiter were returned by the Voyager 1 and 2 spacecraft. Amazingly, Voyagers 1 and 2 are still functioning 45 years after their launch, returning science data from the leading edge of interstellar space. They are further away from Earth than any other man made objects.

In all, more than 60 moons orbit Jupiter, most of them small lumpy irregular potato shapes of rock combined with ice. But the larger moons are unique worlds. Jupiter's moon Io is the most volcanically active body in the solar system. It is constantly rumbling and ejecting noxious sulfur, and sulfur dioxide, into Jupiter's orbit. Io's discharge is responsible for much of the color in Jupiter's beautiful swirling cloud streams and storm systems. Io's volcanism is the result of Jupiter's gravitational tidal forces on the moon, as it rotates and orbits the gas giant. These forces are accentuated by Io's elliptical orbit as it moves closer, and then further from Jupiter in its course.

Moon Europa is a frozen water world that may have twice as much water as Earth. Its crisscrossed icy surface has been formed under the continuous stresses induced by Jupiter's enormous gravitational tides, making it the smoothest planetary body in the solar system. The presence of water, and the smooth surface, have lead scientists to conclude that a water ocean might exist under the surface ice. Europa also has the faintest of atmospheres, mainly and surprisingly, of oxygen. These factors make Europa a prime candidate for rudimentary life forms under its ice sheet.

Saturn is the next gas giant planet out from the Sun, best known by its spectacular system of rings. Carl Sagan called it the "set jewel" of the solar system. The dazzling rings of the sixth planet are composed mostly of chunks of ice with dust, rocky debris, and more than 60 tiny moonlets. These "shepherding" moons corral the relatively light ring material by virtue of their concentrated mass, and give the rings a beautiful groove like complexity.

Saturn's largest moon, Titan, has a diameter about half again larger than the Earth's Moon. Titan has a dense atmosphere of smog-like carbon compounds that form an opaque atmosphere. Were it not so far from the Sun, it would probably be very like the early Earth. Its thick atmosphere blocks a direct view, but JPL spacecraft Cassini has explored its surface using radar, an array of science instruments, and a special landing probe.

Huygens, a European Space Agency probe carried along by Cassini, landed on Titan. There it discovered frigid lakes of liquid methane, complete with shorelines and hydrocarbon rain. At 350°F below zero there is little chance for life on Titan, but it is the only other world we know of with real lakes and rain, albeit of complex hydrocarbons.

Enceladus is only the sixth largest of Saturn's moons, but it is one of the most interesting, owing to huge amounts of water. Water rich plumes vent from the moon's surface at its south pole. Enceladus's orbital wobble has led scientists to conclude that its frozen outer crust floats on a liquid water ocean, which surrounds a rocky core. It is believed that the internal pressure arising from this wobble forces water jets out from the moon's surface.[2] Certainly the inside of the moon is warm enough for liquid water, and that makes Enceladus another candidate host for simple life forms.

The outer most gas giants Uranus, and then Neptune, are great balls of hydrogen, helium and methane gas. They are both unique in that the atmospheric methane has given both planets a beautiful icy cerulean blue color. Neptune has a mass of 17 Earths, while Uranus has a mass of 14 Earths. Yet, Neptune is smaller in diameter than Uranus, owing to its greater mass, and the gravitational compression of its gassy sphere.

One balmy summer evening in 1989 my young family visited Cal Tech to witness the live transmission of Voyager 2 images from Neptune. As we were leaving the campus a small tabby kitten in a box caught the eye of my middle daughter. A couple of students were offering the tiny cat for adoption, and our girls convinced us to take her into our home. My daughters christened her Neptune, on the spot.

Icy rocky Pluto, formerly known as the 9th planet, is now designated as a dwarf planet, with only one fifth the mass of the Earth's Moon. It was demoted ostensibly because Pluto doesn't possess enough gravity to clear its vicinity of planetary debris, owing to its relatively small mass. But the photos of Pluto taken by the New Horizons spacecraft in 2015 look for the world like a planet. So much as a tiny grain of sand could have destroyed New Horizons, but it survived its close flyby encounter with Pluto. So it seems Pluto's local vicinity is actually quite clear of debris.

Pluto, and I will say planet Pluto, orbits the Sun within the distant Kuiper belt—an uncounted number of icy comets and rocky asteroids. Pluto has the company of other dwarf planets Ceres, Haumea, Makemake, and Eris, and there may be other similar planetoids in the Kuiper belt.

A SEASONED AEROSPACE ENGINEER

Thankfully, most of the projects I have supported over the years have been successes. Mission success is sweet, and I do get choked up watching the mission control engineers jubilate over a successful Mars landing. But Mars landings only occur once every couple of years, and at that point in the mission the real science is just getting started.

Typically, a space mission has to persist over the course of several months, even years, in order to produce useful science. I have found that the acute pain of a mission failure comes suddenly, but, as in life, success accumulates one day, one mission, at a time.

While much of the lab was working on the Cassini spacecraft that would orbit Saturn, I worked on a series of space science instruments and contractor supplied spacecraft. I also did a stint generating vibration predictions for the Mars Pathfinder mission. Pathfinder was the first rover to land on Mars, and navigate autonomously to investigate otherworldly rocks and boulders. Its July 4th landing on Mars in 1996 was a stunning success that instilled a sense of pride in everyone at JPL.

This success was followed by the Mars Global Surveyor spacecraft that would operate in Mars orbit for more than 10 years. About that time, I designed the spacecraft vibration test program for Deep Space 1, which successfully flew by comet Borrelly.

A few years after the first PMIRR instrument was lost with Mars Observer, the PMIRR II team asked me to conduct the random vibration test on their replacement instrument. It was to be launched on the Mars Climate Orbiter mission. After the successful completion of PMIRR II's vibration test, I thanked the team for allowing me the opportunity to perform their test. I knew they had their choice of test engineers. Finally, I felt as though I had gotten a monkey off my back, redeeming myself after the first PMIRR Cooler vibration test failure.

Still, by 1998 I thought the grass might be greener elsewhere. The ghost of Mars Observer, that consumed so much of my career, still haunted me. California was an expensive place to raise three daughters, and I was becoming increasingly frustrated by my growing home mortgage that was used to cover my family's living expenses.

I decided to try a fresh start at Boeing's Delta II rocket division. In exchange, I got a decent raise and a principal engineer's position. I was part of a team that redesigned the center body section of the Delta II rocket. After a year and a half of analysis, aluminum machining and test planning, I conducted an acoustic test of the new rocket section. The test verified my predictions that the existing rocket control equipment, housed in the center body, did not have to be re-qualified, except for one small valve.

It was gratifying to see the project move successfully from concept drawings to working hardware. The new center body increased the launch capability of the Delta II rocket tremendously, widening the range of weather conditions permitted for a Delta II launch. The Delta II management was happy, and so was I.

But while I was at Boeing the unmanned space program took another turn for the worse on September 23, 1999. Like the return of a curse, the PMIRR II instrument (I had tested at JPL months before) was destroyed when the Mars Climate Orbiter burned up in the Martian atmosphere, instead of entering Mars orbit. This occurred because the units of the navigation parameters were not properly communicated between the spacecraft contractor and the JPL navigation team. I could scarcely believe it, but I knew how the navigation team must have felt.

Since I had vibration tested an instrument on the spacecraft, my wife and I had been invited guests at JPL the night the Climate Orbiter was to enter Mars orbit. The mood quickly became somber as the realization sunk in that the spacecraft had been lost. Then disaster piled upon disaster. Just ten weeks later on December 3, the Mars Polar Lander crashed into the Martian surface when its landing rockets shut down prematurely.

It cushioned the blow for me somewhat to be working at Boeing, but I knew my time there was coming to a close. I found the company culture difficult, and the Delta rocket division did not look financially healthy. Whole sections of the plant were being moved out of California, and it seemed to me only a matter of time before the engineering staff would be transferred out of state, as well.

In spite of the battle scars left by test and space mission failures, I wanted to go back to JPL for which my skills and experience were tailored. My former boss Dennis Kern was willing to take me back into my old work group, and after 6 months of waiting for the right paper work, I was back on lab. More money in my paycheck didn't hurt either.

Over the next several years I worked on science instruments that would support Earth orbiting satellites, and deep space missions. Each project helped me hone my skills in force limited vibration testing, and project support. I also supported complete spacecraft projects like CloudSat, and DAWN. Later, I vibration tested the powerful HiRise telescope for the highly successful Mars Reconnaissance Orbiter.

Then in 2003 another manned space disaster occurred. The Space Shuttle Columbia was damaged on lift off when water saturated foam, from its main fuel tank, tore loose and punctured the leading edge of its left wing. Engineers on the ground knew foam had hit the wing. They had photos. But in a case of willful blindness NASA managers decided not to inspect the Shuttle wing for damage. They convinced themselves that serious damage to the orbiter was not likely, and that no repair was possible in any event. Foam had come off the main fuel tank before with no ill effect on the Shuttle.

Sixteen days later, when Columbia reentered Earth's atmosphere, super hot plasma entered the damaged left wing and incinerated the Shuttle with the loss of all 7 astronauts. It had been seventeen years since Space Shuttle Challenger had blown up. I felt sick to my stomach and I was depressed for days. It felt like loosing a close relative.

The Shuttle program stood down for a second time to regroup. The process consumed more than two years, but this time there were no JPL missions dependent on the Shuttle. The direct impact on JPL programs would be minimal, but the Shuttle recovery effort would siphon money away from several other NASA programs.

The Space Shuttle did fly again, but this was the beginning of the end. The Shuttle program was canceled in 2011, and the United States was not able to launch people into Earth orbit for nine long years. In the meantime we had to buy seats to our own space station on Russian rockets. At this writing the United States is still not able to fly people beyond the bounds of Earth's gravity. We have not had that capability since the last manned Moon landing in 1972, 50 years ago. Now, however, with a renewed launch capability the American manned space program seems to have a new sense of purpose, centered on the Moon and Mars.

About the time the Shuttle started flying again, I was called away to Long Island for a series of lengthy vibration test campaigns on ultra light fuel tanks. I enjoyed my wife's support on these long trips away from home. She was able to travel more with me since the kids were out of the house. Long Island was a really nice area to explore after hours, and on weekends we saw the Montauk lighthouse and the Hamptons.

I also had a new project, the Orbiting Carbon Observatory (OCO). OCO was a small spacecraft with a single instrument that was designed to monitor the Earth's carbon cycle. The burning of fossil fuels and the rotting of plants release carbon dioxide into the air. Living plants on land and sea metabolize carbon dioxide, removing it from the atmosphere. In simplified form, this is the carbon cycle.

Over the next four years I would travel to Orbital Sciences in Virginia for numerous meetings and system tests before program's end. I enjoyed the work, the location and the people. At the project's completion, I had planned to travel to Vandenberg Air Force Base with my wife to watch the OCO launch, but something kept me from signing up with the JPL trip administrator.

Instead, I was performing a vibration test at JPL on the day the OCO rocket was launched. Word of what happened spread quickly throughout the laboratory. The aerodynamic fairing around the spacecraft failed to open while the upper stage of the rocket was still firing. The unintended weight of the errant fairing combined with that of the spacecraft caused OCO to plunge into the Antarctic Ocean, instead of achieving Earth orbit. The failure did not hurt as much as the earlier losses, but it was discouraging to know that four more years of my career had just crashed into the sea. At least no people had been killed.

In the meantime, I became involved in the Mars Science Laboratory project, now known as the Curiosity Mars rover. I participated in RTG (Radio Thermal Generator) shock testing, and then I co-directed the rover's vibration test.

NASA and congress decided to fund a re-flight of the OCO mission that had been lost. The announcement was a relief. It was a chance to recoup the countless years of labor of the OCO engineers and scientists. Because of the Earth's climate change, scientific study of the Earth's carbon cycle was considered important enough to warrant this added expenditure. For me it was a chance to work more closely with the project office, and develop close working relationships with some very fine engineers. The OCO-2 project level managers were demanding, but their patience and heart felt appreciation was gratifying. It was my best project experience.

Thankfully, OCO-2 was successfully launched in July of 2014 on a Delta II, using 'my' new rocket center body. An encouraging success, OCO-2 is still orbiting Earth taking carbon cycle data and relaying it back to Earth.

ASTEROIDS, COMETS AND PROPHECY

American planetary science has in our day fulfilled the prophecy of Christ about great signs in the heavens. More and varied great signs are sure to come. But what of the terrors of which He spoke? Terror enough is found in the asteroids and comets in the deep reaches of the solar system.

Asteroids and comets pose a grave danger to the future of our planet—a far greater danger than global warming. The Bible does prophesy an extreme episode of global warming, one caused by a spectacular outburst of the Sun sometime in the future. Revelation 16:8 says, "The fourth angel poured out his bowl on the sun, and it was allowed to scorch people with fire."[3] But, the stark truth is that an asteroid or comet impact has the potential to plunge the Earth into another ice age, or even wipe out most Earth life.

Catastrophic extinction impact events have occurred on the Earth in the distant past, and the Earth still bears the scars of many of these massive impacts. The last really large one hit what is now Chicxulub, Mexico, 65 million years ago leaving a crater 110 miles wide. It killed off the large dinosaurs, which allowed mammals and human beings to arise and prosper. Layers of meteor impact trace elements in soil sediments from around the world, testify to the global influence of this impact event.

Meteor Crater in Arizona is a young and sizable crater, the like of which is typically only found on distant planets and moons. You can stand at its rim and look down its craggy slopes to the crater floor. It is an impressive and sobering sight.

Human beings have now witnessed comet impacts first hand, and what a sight! Astronomers watched in amazement in 1994 as comet Shoemaker Levy broke apart under the tidal forces of Jupiter's gravity. Then, piece by massive piece, the fragmented comet hit Jupiter like a barrage of super atomic bombs, with a combined power hundreds of times greater than Earth's entire nuclear arsenal.[4]

I marveled at the impact scars in the clouds of Jupiter, viewed through a telescope set up by volunteers at the Griffith Park Observatory. It was sobering to see the aftermath of a series of impacts that would have caused unthinkable damage and death had they occurred on the Earth.

Other more recent impact events have also been discovered. In July 2009, a comet strike of Jupiter was observed, after the fact, using Hubble Space Telescope images. Since 1990, the Ulysses and SOHO solar observatories have recorded comets hitting or grazing the Sun in dramatic fashion, one as recently as May 11, 2011. Just a few days later on July 6, 2011, NASA's Solar Dynamics Observatory captured the first image of a comet disintegrating in the Sun's upper atmosphere.[5]

Fortunately for us, most of the comets and asteroids that wander through our space hit the Sun, or one of the gas giant planets like Jupiter or Saturn. The Earth's relatively small size, and the Moon's gravitational pull, are our last lines of defense against these impact events. Yet, statistically, it is not a question of if another killer impact will occur on Earth, but when. The long-term likelihood of such an impact event prompted Stephen Hawking to say that humans must begin to migrate into space to ensure mankind's long term survival.[6]

Indeed, some of the events prophesied in Revelation sound exactly like comet and asteroid impact events. In the book of Revelation, it says, "something like a great mountain, burning with fire, was thrown into the sea ... and a great star fell from heaven, blazing like a torch, and it fell on a third of the rivers and on the springs of water."[7] These events were described hundreds of years before people knew the real nature of asteroids and comets, and long before we knew there is a high likelihood that such an impact would hit a body of water.

There is an asteroid named Apophis that will make a near Earth pass in 2029, and then come a good deal closer in 2036. There are thousands of similar bodies that are yet undiscovered.[8] One of them could strike the Earth with very little warning. We have already had close calls.

In February 2013, a meteor of only 20 meters in length unexpectedly exploded 15 miles above the Russian Urals. It released the energy of 25 Hiroshima atomic bombs in one-and-a-half seconds.[9] The blast damaged buildings and injured hundreds of people. Had this undetected asteroid entered the Earth's atmosphere at a steeper angle over a city, the devastation could have been staggering. Astrophysicist have shown conclusively that Sodom, at Tall el-Hammam, was destroyed by such a cosmic airburst. Therefore, it behooves us to continue developing space technology, both human and robotic, to do what is possible to avoid a catastrophic asteroid or comet strike.

Critics of the Church say the prophecies of Revelation are dangerous— that they can be self-fulfilling. Yet, the most terrible events of Revelation are acts of God. No man can make an asteroid or comet hit the Earth. Furthermore, anyone who would start a nuclear conflagration would not be acting by Christian principles, but by the all too-human motivations of greed, power and murder. Moreover, all these things will come about at a time when the influence of the Church has been minimized in a great apostasy, that has already begun.[10]

Science offers no guarantees, but God has promised that mankind will not be wiped out by killer impact events, or by war. Jesus prophesied that mankind will be spared during a time of unparalleled trial yet to come, "For then there will be great tribulation, such as has not been from the beginning of the world until now, no, and never will be. And if those days had not been cut short, no human being would be saved. But for the sake of the elect those days will be cut short."[11]

God will see His people through any peril, for the apocalypse described in the Bible is not an end of humanity—it is a new beginning.

CHAPTER SIX

A BEGINNING & AN END OF ALL THINGS

"It was My hands that stretched out the heavens, and I commanded all their host." ~ Isaiah 45:12 (ESV)

The Big Bang creation event produced an unimaginable number of extremely energetic photons from nothing, in a sudden burst. The discovery of the Big Bang rocked the world of astronomy because it implied a genesis of the universe. Before this, most modern scientists, like Einstein, were of the opinion that the universe was static and eternal. Stephen Hawking suggested a motivation for this view, writing, "Many people do not like the idea that time has a beginning, probably because it smacks of divine intervention."[1]

The Big Bang had been theorized long before it was discovered. Scientists knew a tell tale sign of such a creation event would be a ubiquitous remnant of the initial radiation, a kind of low level radio "noise", visible even after billions of years. Theory predicted that the expansion of the universe would have stretched the wavelengths of the initial radiation a million-million times, into much longer and colder microwaves. In our epoch, this radiation should be just a few degrees above absolute zero temperature, and it would look essentially the same in every direction of space.

Then in 1964, astronomers Arno Penzias and Robert Wilson discovered the Cosmic Background Radiation, quite by accident while conducting microwave measurements.[2] They found a pervasive microwave background 'noise' with an extremely cold temperature, only 2.7° Kelvin, and it seemed to emanate from space itself. Penzias and Wilson quickly realized this was evidence for the maligned Big Bang theory, and for this they shared the Noble Prize.

Later in 1989, George Smoot and other scientists of the Cosmic Background Explorer (COBE) satellite program discovered that variations of the background radiation across the sky are exceedingly small, with temperature variations of only 1 part per 100,000. These differences look like ripples in a temperature map of the sky.[3] This finding, together with the expansion of the universe, indicated that all parts of the sky had been in direct contact in the distant past. There was a common source for everything. In other words, the Genesis claim of a beginning was verified experimentally.

COBE data confirmed the theory that the background radiation behaves like a perfect blackbody radiator—the best possible emitter of thermal radiation.[4] This proved that the background radiation originated with the universe at large (space itself) and not with distant stars.[5] David Schramm of the University of Chicago says that the black body radiator characteristic means, "that the universe was once so dense that it was a single, continuous body in thermal equilibrium, one that could be characterized by a single temperature."[6] This means that the universe started long ago as a single point.

The NASA COBE team explains it further, "This observation matches the predictions of the hot Big Bang theory extraordinarily well, and indicates that nearly all of the radiant energy of the Universe was released within the first year after the Big Bang."[7]

More sensitive measurements of the background radiation, by the Wilkinson Microwave Anisotropy Probe (WMAP) and Planck spacecraft, provided an analysis of the material content of the universe, from 380,000 years after the Big Bang to the present.[8] The relative abundance of the atomic elements in space —hydrogen, helium, carbon and oxygen—also confirmed the hot Big Bang theory over other "eternal" universes.

These discoveries essentially forced cosmology into agreement with the Old Testament book of Genesis. Astrophysicist George Smoot said, "If you're religious, it's like looking at God." Reporter Fred Heeren writes, "Stephen Hawking, whose own work had recently sought alternatives to a universe with a beginning, couldn't have been more impressed with the findings. He called them "the most important discovery of the century, if not of all time.""[9]

Robert Wilson, co-discoverer of the cosmic background radiation, told Heeren, "Certainly there was something that set it all off. Certainly, if you are religious, I can't think of a better theory of the origin of the universe to match with Genesis."[10] Scientist Hugh Ross marvels that, "The beginning of the universe exposes the greatest miracle imaginable."[11] Distinguished astronomer Robert Jastrow, apparently not a believer, also said, "There is no doubt that a parallel exists between the Big Bang as an event and the Christian notion of creation from nothing."[12]

Therefore, background radiation observations form a stunning confirmation of the Biblical account of creation. The Ancient of Days caused the universe to spring out of nothingness and expand, just as described in the book of Job, "He alone has spread out the heavens."[13]

There is another divine parallel with the Cosmic Background Radiation. Astronomers can measure Earth's velocity relative to the primordial light of the Big Bang by measuring its red frequency shift. Anyone at any other location in the universe could make the same measurement, making the background radiation a kind of universal reference. In the same way, we can all tell how far we are away from God's universal moral reference—the Ten Commandments. God causes the light of His truth to shine on all people, no matter what their spiritual position is.

The universality of the cosmic background radiation is like the all present nature of God—Yahweh Shammah—"the Lord is there."[14] The Lord is always ready to be found.

Some Christians do not like the idea of a Big Bang universe. They argue that God created the universe with an apparent age; that it looks ancient but is actually quite young. Many even insist there is plenty of evidence for a young universe, but there is no such scientific evidence. Hugh Ross summarized his argument against the young universe, "when these 'evidences' of youthfulness are examined and analyzed, they reveal one or more of the following: 1) faulty assumptions, 2) faulty data, 3) misapplication of principles, laws, and equations, and 4) ignorance of mitigating evidence."[15] The motivation for the young Earth view of the cosmos is to prop up an over simplified interpretation of Genesis.

Consider that when astronomers look into space they are looking back in time. Scientists can easily demonstrate that the universe is vastly older than 6000 years. In fact, the light just now reaching us from some of the most remote stars has been in transit for more than 12 billion years. Based on light from massively bright Super Nova – explosive stellar cataclysms - astronomers have estimated the age of the universe to be 13.7 billion years, give or take a few tenths.

There is also the long term cooling of the Big Bang radiation, which began at trillions of degrees. It is now just 2.7° Kelvin above absolute zero temperature, due to the expansion of space.

Why would God create the appearance of a genesis event 13.7 billion years ago if it occurred 6000 years ago, as young Earth believers claim? Would God wish to deceive us? A nearly limitless number of details, from the remnant radiation of the Big Bang, to the light from the earliest most distant stars and developing galaxies, trace the history of the creation process in deep space. The history of how the universe developed over time is literally contained within the heavens and in the Earth.

On the other hand, hoping to eliminate God, atheistic scientists liken the creation event to a quantum mechanical fluctuation. This is a naturally occurring spontaneous 'coming and going' of quantum energy in the vacuum of space. Yet predictions show such a universe would have only lasted a few millionths of a second before winking back out of existence.[16] Quantum physics cannot say why, or how the universe came into being. It simply describes the unfolding of the universe.[17]

Recently Stephen Hawking declared that gravity and physics alone created the universe spontaneously, and that God is not needed to create the universe.[18] In a similar vein, Vlatko Vedral maintains that information spontaneously "created itself" and then brought the universe into existence.[19] The claim is that an unimaginably vast number of universes were created by this mechanism, each one with different physical laws. At least one of these universes is supposed to have the natural laws that are required to make the unlikely occurrence of life possible, strictly by chance.

This proposal seems to be based on the idea that information can exist in its own right, without matter or energy.

But, information has never been observed as "disembodied" from energy or matter. This is more like believing in the immortality of the human soul—not what we have come to expect of agnostic scientists. Still, if Hawking and Vedral are correct in saying information created the universe (and at this point it is an unproven scientific speculation), it would be the handiwork of a grander soul than ours. It would be a manifestation of the Creator.

The experimental evidence is that in nearly 14 billion light years of time and space, no other Big Bang has ever been found. There is no evidence of contact with other universes in the background radiation left over from the Big Bang. There is no evidence that other universes have self-generated within our view. Instead, all the data from astronomy indicates that all the universe's energy began at one place, a point called the Initial Singularity. From that singular point came all the possibilities, energy and material for everything and everyone that would ever come into existence.

THE SINGULARITY

The Initial Singularity was not just the beginning of matter and energy, but it was also the beginning of time and space.[20] According to quantum mechanics theory, the smallest division of time is Planck time, an unimaginably short duration of 10^{-43} seconds. For all practical purposes, events separated by a duration of Planck time are instantaneous. Scientists believe they have worked out how the universe unfolded from one Planck unit of time forward. Yet, no one knows what happened before this because our scientific equations and observations break down at the singularity, the beginning.

Information theory indicates that in the very beginning, at the singularity, the universe may have contained only a few bits of information, perhaps no information at all—it was truly void.[21] This meshes precisely with the Genesis account. No information at the beginning is equivalent to saying that entropy, a measure of disorder, was at an absolute minimum at the singularity, so that there was no disorder at the moment of Creation. This reflects another aspect of God's character, for there is no unclean thing in God.[22] In other words, there is no disorder in Him. We might readily expect the intersection of a perfect God and the universe to have no disorder at all.

Though the Genesis account is Earth centric, it does not begin with the formation of the Earth, as one might expect of an ancient pre-science storyteller. It is significant that Genesis 1:1 puts the heavens ahead of the Earth, in the proper order of creation, "In the beginning God created the heavens and the Earth."[23]

Genesis 1:2 is beautifully evocative of the early universe after the Big Bang, "The earth was without form and void and darkness was on the face of the deep and the Spirit of God was hovering over the face of the waters (brooding, conceiving, planning)."[24] Before the universe existed, there was no material thing. Matter and the Earth had not yet been formed, but space was void and empty.

Physicist Frank Tipler makes the stunning claim that the initial singularity is an exact scientific description of God, equating the singularity with God. Tipler says, "Stephen Hawking proved mathematically that the Singularity is not in time or in space, but outside both. In other words, the Singularity is transcendent to space and time. According to the theologian Thomas Aquinas, "God created the Universe" means simply that all causal chains begin in God ... The Cosmological Singularity is the Judeo-Christian God.[25]

To some this might appear to be heresy, but a careful consideration of the facts shows this is not so. Physical laws yield infinitely large answers at the very beginning of space and time—at the Initial Singularity. That is, the answers become physically meaningless at the Singularity. Moreover, the beginning of the universe is also unknowable by any experiment. The Initial Singularity is that from which every possibility, all energy, and all matter came. Therefore, if God is the outside agent that started the universe, as a matter of physics, He could be described as the Initial Singularity—the Alpha, the Indescribable One.

More accurately, the Initial Singularity is the place where God, who is Spirit, intersects the physical universe causing the universe to exist. The mathematical inexpressibility of the Singularity is the intersection of science and God; the physical intersection of the Singularity with time and space is God's direct action in creation. God created the universe, but He is not a part of the universe, just as the Initial Singularity is not part of the universe. It is ironic, then, that many people say they do not believe in God because He is not detectable in the universe.

Tipler observes that the Initial Singularity has an immensely important function in physics: "the Cosmological Singularity stabilizes the cosmos."[26] He says that without the Initial Singularity the equations of physics would be unresolvable inside the universe. In a very real sense, then, the physics of cosmology models the creative act of God. This is one of the strongest proof marks of God in all science.

The agreement of Genesis and science is not a superficial matter; it is in the fabric of cosmology. Ancient Jewish Bible scholars were able to glean a very modern description of the universe's first moments from the text of Genesis, 800 years ago, long before modern science.

Gerald Schroeder recounts that, "Nahmanides, in the year 1250, described the process with uncanny accuracy: the initial creation produced an entity so thin it had no substance to it. ... As the universe expanded from the size of that initial minuscule space, the primordial substanceless substance changed into matter, as we know it. Biblical time, he continued, starts ('grabs hold' in his words) with the appearance of matter. ... Nahmanides writes that his teachers learned this account from the first word of the bible, beraesheet, which means "In the beginning of". In the beginning of what, they asked? In the beginning of time was their conclusion."[27] That ancient Jewish commentators could deduce these things, strictly from the Genesis text is a strong corroboration of Divine revelation.

THE EARLY UNIVERSE

The universe did start with a "primordial substanceless substance" called energy, just as Genesis 1:3-5 says. "And God said, 'Let there be light,"[28] and there was light. Moreover, it is extraordinary that the creation of light was not related directly to the Sun by the author of Genesis, as it might easily have been.

Instead, in Genesis light energy is the first real describable thing in its own right, matching the scientific account.

Science says that matter came into existence just a few moments after the Big Bang, condensing out of the energy field as the infant universe expanded. Einstein proved mathematically in the early 20th century that energy and matter are actually different forms of the same thing. This was forcibly demonstrated by the atomic bomb in 1945.

Matter and energy, being of the same substance, is similar to God's Word being of the same substance as God. God, who is an energy-like Spirit, created the physical world by His word. Then He sent His Word into the world as the flesh-and-blood person of Jesus Christ to live among us, and tell us the truth about the Father. For this reason Jesus said, "I am the light of the world."[29] He is the material One who dispels the spiritual darkness in the world.

The earliest matter to appear in the primordial universe was super hot and dense. It was a sort of liquid, in the form of a quark-gluon plasma. Quarks are fundamental particles of matter that combine to make neutrons and protons, two of the basic components of atoms.[30] Scientists know what this primordial space liquid was like. It has been observed in high energy physics laboratories that, for a brief moment, produce particle energies high enough for the constituent quarks to become free of their atomic bonds.

Mark Peplow writes that, "The resulting liquid is almost 'perfect': it has a very low viscosity and is so uniform that it looks the same from any angle."[31] Waves propagated through the quark liquid of the early universe like sound waves in water. These waves and ripples in the quark plasma produced very slight variations. These density variations eventually led to regions of space with slightly higher or lower concentrations of mass.

Amazingly, Genesis 1:6-7 also describes the first matter in the heavens in terms of a liquid, "God made the expanse and separated the 'waters' that were under the expanse from the 'waters' that were above the expanse."[32] The waves and ripples in the early universe must have sounded like music to God's ear, as it says in Isaiah 49:13, "Sing for joy, O heavens, and exult!"[33]

The newborn universe grew during a period of rapid expansion called “Inflation”, setting the stage for the current enormity of the universe.[34] The inflationary expansion of space was driven by energy released in a kind of state transition, as the universe cooled. This was similar to the way energy is released when ice condenses out of chilled water. When the state transition was complete, the universe slowed to a lower rate of expansion. The inflationary expansion took place in only a tiny fraction of a second after the Big Bang. Yet, inflation theory matches the COBE and WMAP deep space observations exactly.

The notion of a rapid and continuous expansion of space is mentioned in Jeremiah, “It is He who made the earth by His power, who established the world by His wisdom, and by His understanding stretched out the heavens.”[35] As the inflationary universe expanded 1,000 times, the early quark- gluon plasma cooled, and protons and neutrons began to form. Quarks and gluons have been locked up within protons and neutrons ever since. As the universe cooled another 1000 times, light atomic nuclei formed.[36]

As space expanded further, free electrons were finally captured by atomic nuclei, creating electrically neutral atoms—complete atoms—for the first time. At that moment, the soupy opaque universe immediately transitioned to a transparent form, and light began to propagate through the fledgling universe unimpeded. This occurred when the universe was about 380,000 years old.[37] The narrative of Genesis 1:4-5 seems to describe this event saying, “And God separated the light from the darkness.”[38]

The earliest complete atoms were mostly the lighter elements, hydrogen, helium and deuterium with only a small amount of lithium.[39] Stable atoms have persisted since that early time, unchanged for 13.7 billion years. In this way, the unchanging nature of God’s word is made evident in the stability of these unseen atomic building blocks.

Genesis 1:6-7 also correctly describes the expansive nature of the growing universe, “God made the expanse and separated the ‘waters’ that were under the expanse from the ‘waters’ that were above the expanse.”[40] This evokes the separation of matter from the empty regions of the fledgling universe. The current configuration of galaxy clusters and empty space evolved from these density variations of matter in space.

In that early epoch, there were no stars in the heavens, and as the background radiation dimmed, darkness prevailed in the early universe. Darkness lasted a few million years until the first stars coalesced from the material of the Big Bang, and ignited. This ushered in the current era of sustained starlight in the universe. Billions of stars formed in clusters that comprised the earliest galaxies, which were spread out through the heavens. Genesis 1:8 marks the completion of the form of the heavens, "and God called the expanse heaven."[41] Genesis correctly puts all heavenly bodies into the modern perspective—planetary objects that give light and mark seasons, and not as ancient gods.

Many of the first stars were massive in the extreme, a hundred times greater in size than the Sun, and they burned hot and fast. These stars went through their nuclear fuel in only a few million years, while forming some of the heavier atomic elements. Then these stars went Supernova, they exploded away their outer shells of hydrogen and helium, along with a host of other elements necessary for life like oxygen, iron and carbon. These resource rich dust clouds, blown into space by the earliest spent stars, made it possible for other more modern stars and planetary systems like ours to form. Only this later generation of stars possessed the atomic elements necessary to support life.

The Sun, the Earth and the Moon formed from these first generation star materials, within a long-gone dust cloud. This is described in Genesis 1:9-10, "And God said, 'Let the waters under the heavens be gathered together into one place, and let the dry land appear.' And it was so. God called the dry land Earth, and the waters that were gathered together He called Seas. And God saw that it was good."[42] So, the Earth was finally established.

From here the scientific account of the early universe takes a strange turn, even to modern ears. The material construction of everything we know and see, including all the stars in all the galaxies in deep space, constitutes only a small portion of the mass that exists. Ordinary matter—every substance we are familiar with—seems to account for only 4–7% of the mass of the universe.

Dark matter is a strange non-standard material referred to as non-baryonic matter, and it is significantly more plentiful than normal matter. Most of the universe seems to be something besides that of which you and I are made.[43] Dark matter is too cold to detect in deep space. It does not glow or reflect light, and so far dark matter has only been detected indirectly by observing its gravitational effects on light from stars and galaxies.

To be sure, some 'dark matter' is comprised of normal matter contained in cool planetary bodies like Brown Dwarfs and Red Dwarfs. Brown Dwarfs, a class of planetary bodies, are too small to sustain nuclear fusion and are, therefore, dark. Red Dwarf stars have only a fraction of the mass of the Sun, and burn very dimly. These dwarf stars are so numerous there may be three times more stars in the universe than previously supposed.

But there is more to dark matter than this.[44] Astronomers generally agree that galaxies do not have enough ordinary mass to hold their shape over time; the stars within them should have drifted apart.[45] It's no surprise then that scientists say that dark matter's gravitational effects dominate the process of galaxy formation in the universe.[46]

Maps of dark matter are currently being generated from the latest deep space observations, but scientists still do not know what dark matter is. Dark matter appears to be unevenly distributed in the universe, and it may be more prevalent in certain types of galaxies, like smaller star clusters.[47]

There are ongoing experiments designed to directly detect dark matter deep underground, but to date results have been inconclusive. Dark matter is exceptionally hard to detect with instruments since it interacts poorly with normal matter. Therefore, most of the information we have about dark matter has been inferred from deep space observations of mass concentrations. Yet dark matter is not the strangest thing about the universe at large.

THE ACCELERATING UNIVERSE

One of the most startling discoveries of modern astronomy is that the universe is not just expanding, but that the volume of space is growing at an ever accelerating rate. A mysterious dark energy has been pushing the galaxies of the universe further apart, and its force has been getting stronger with time. Indeed, it is the most abundant thing in the universe. It may seem strange that any kind of energy could be the most plentiful "thing" in the universe. But in the earliest universe there was nothing except energy and information.

Dark energy acts like the Cosmological Constant in Einstein's general relativity, making the volume of space expand.[48] Just like dark matter, dark energy has not been directly measured, but its existence has been surmised by its anti gravitational effect on distant galaxies. This is the reverse of the gravitational attraction attributed to dark matter.

Mario Livio explains how Dark Energy was discovered, "two teams observed and analyzed a few tens of supernovae, at a range of distances spanning a corresponding time interval of about one-half the age of the universe. The results of these analyses came as a shock ... Not only is our universe flying apart, but it does so at ever-greater speeds. ... No wonder that Science magazine selected the accelerating universe as their major 'Breakthrough of the Year.'"[49] This expansion has been confirmed by the James Webb telescope.

The accelerating expansion of the volume of space, combined with the early epoch of inflation, means the universe has grown faster than the speed of light. So the current best estimate of the size of the universe is 156 billion light years across! This result is based on COBE and WMAP measurements of the Cosmic Background Radiation.[50] The universe has been expanding so quickly there are distant parts of it that we will never be able to see.

While there is no general consensus on what dark energy is, it is agreed that it acts as an anti-gravity force, pushing all the galaxies in the universe outward in an accelerating expansion. It is at once humbling and exciting to know there are still some basic phenomena, the physics of which are not yet well understood.

The upshot of the discovery of the universe's accelerating expansion is that the universe is now seen to have an end. Mario Livio understandably laments the end of the universe, "as long as (the cosmological constant) is not negative, the universe is going to expand forever. Such an eternal expansion can most probably lead to only one 'sad' ending: a cold death!"[51]

The accelerating universe will continue to cool down as empty space grows, and galaxies will be pushed further and further apart. Several billions of years hence, the acceleration of the cosmos may eventually rip apart galaxies, solar systems, planets, stars and then finally even molecules, until a sort of heat death of the universe occurs.

The Bible predicted thousands of years ago that the heavens would pass away. Jesus said, "Heaven and earth will pass away, but My words will not pass away."[52] Psalm 102:25-26 says, "the heavens are the work of Your hands. They will perish, but You will endure; yes, they will all grow old like a garment."[53] Now science agrees that the universe will grow old and wear out.

Modern cosmologists like Carl Sagan once believed that gravity's power would eventually halt the universe's expansion, pull in the universe to collapse on itself, and then rebound to create another Big Bang, resulting in another universe. Most scientists gladly embraced this self-regenerating universe theory, but it has proven to be incorrect. Instead, all the physical evidence now points to the familiar narrative of Genesis, and the expanding universe of Jeremiah. The idea of a universe that recycles itself has turned out to be the fantasy, instead of Genesis.

Not to worry, the demise of planet Earth is probably billions of years off. When the Sun burns up most of its hydrogen fuel, its core will contract and heat up until helium fusion begins, as the core temperature reaches around 100,000,000° Kelvin. The resulting increase in internal pressure will cause the Sun to expand and become a Red Giant star. At that time the Sun's surface will expand out as far as the orbit of Mars, and its perimeter will engulf the Earth. In the long run, human beings will have to leave the planet to ensure the survival of the human race, unless God changes the course of natural events (He has promised to save humanity).

Mario Livio believes the implication of an eternally expanding universe is not "beautiful", meaning that there is no beautiful stand-alone scientific theory to explain the universe.[54] Indirectly, he laments the fact that the universe had a beginning by a mechanism that does not seem natural, and that it will have an end. We are left with the mystery of Genesis.

To be blunt, a Creator is implied by the central facts of the universe. This is not beautiful to an atheist, but to me a universe with a beginning and an end—with finely tuned physical laws—is extravagantly beautiful. Ours is a universe that points unambiguously to an All Powerful God of vast creativity, immensity, radiance, intellect, terrible power and glory—Elohim.[55] One man's ugliness really is another man's beauty.

THE BIBLE IS UNIQUE

Believers can, in our day, claim that science and the Bible agree on three of the most basic things possible, that the universe had a beginning in the distant past, that the heavens will pass away, and that there will be a fiery end of the Earth.[56] The Divine implications from deep space science, then, are really quite inescapable. The Initial Singularity, that defies mathematical description, is God's intersection with the universe that brings about space and time, and everything that exists.

The correlation of Genesis and science, in general terms, is unique among the religious writings of the world, and this points to a supernatural source of information, that was otherwise unavailable at the time the Bible was written.[57] This should increase our confidence in the Bible and in Christianity. It has for me.

We can trust what God has told us about Himself, and that He will save those who trust Him. The unchanging nature of physical law, and the constancy of the age old universe testify that God is dependable and trustworthy. As it says in Psalms, "Your faithfulness You shall establish in the very heavens."[58] God does not change His mind, and He has imprinted this characteristic into the heavens. We can take Him at His word.

We Christians can have confidence because the predictions of the Bible take us all the way to the end of time—literally to the end of the universe— reassuring us that God will be there for His people. As Jesus Christ said, "I am with you always, to the end of the age."[59] For sure, He has promised that neither calamity, nor the Earth's demise will be the end of mankind, or of those who trust in God. We can rest on the scripture that says there will be a new heaven and a new earth—"Now I saw a new heaven and a new earth, for the first heaven and the first earth had passed away."[60] Isaiah foretells the same thing, "For behold, I create new heavens and a new earth."[61]

Scientists would like to find a new heaven and a new earth — a regeneration of the existing universe—but all they can see is an end to this world, along with the end of human striving. The atheist sees no purpose in the universe, or in life. In stark contrast, believers see real value in life, and we have confidence that God will provide for His people in this world and in the next!

CHAPTER SEVEN

SUBSTRATUM OF THE UNIVERSE

"By faith we understand that the universe was created by the word of God, so that what is seen was not made out of things that are visible."
~ Hebrews 11:3 (ESV)

Albert Einstein's masterworks, the special and general theories of relativity, revolutionized the way we understand time, space, and gravity. His theories went beyond Michelson's famous experiment which established that the speed of light, in a vacuum, is independent of direction.[1]

SPECIAL RELATIVITY AND TIME DILATION

Einstein was the first to deduce that the speed of light is the same for all observers, no matter how fast, or in which direction they are moving.[2] This means light speed is a fundamental constant of nature, a reference speed if you will. In fact, time and space do not have a complete meaning apart from the speed of light. This may strike you as odd, but the peculiar consequences of Einstein's theories are among the most rigorously tested of physical theories.

Einstein believed that "Relativity applies to physics, not ethics," but people still take the theory of relativity as a basis for moral relativity. However, the universal reference of light speed mirrors God as the universal reference for humanity. God is the one by Whom we can measure our existence, allowing us to make sense of life. Because God exists, we can know there are universal moral standards, just as light speed is a universal reference in the physical realm.

The constancy of light speed for all observers is not an esoteric property, but it has some profound physical consequences for time and space that are as peculiar as anything in Alice's Wonderland. However, these consequences only become significant at extremely high velocities near the speed of light. Even so, space engineers must synchronize spacecraft clocks orbiting the Earth, using Einstein's equations. Deep space navigation must be corrected by the same kind of relativistic calculations.

The relativity of time works like this. Imagine a rocket firing its engine long enough that it achieves a velocity that is within a few percent of the speed of light. Time inside the vessel would begin to move more slowly than for an observer on the Earth. The clock's second hand in the rocket would actually tick more slowly than a clock on Earth.[3] Time is said to dilate for the astronaut in the rocket moving near the speed of light. Infinitely near the speed of light time begins to stand still.

In Einstein's famous "twin paradox", one of a pair of twins is in a rocket speeding away through space to a distant star, while her sibling stays on Earth.[4] Time within the rocket begins slowing down relative to the earthbound twin, as the rocket gets closer to the speed of light. Through a TV broadcast, the twin on the ground can see his sister in the rocket moving in slow motion. The sister in the rocket would be completely unaware of this time dilation and would simply go about life, yet she would be aging at a slower rate than her brother.

After several years in space, the speeding rocket returns to Earth, and the girl astronaut emerges from the rocket having aged fewer years than her brother. This kind of outcome has been tested with spacecraft clocks of exquisite precision—this is not science fiction or speculation. The difference in the passage of time for observers at different velocities is real.

Technically, a rocket can never really reach the speed of light without being converted entirely to radiant light energy. Strangely, objects become heavier as they accelerate to speeds near the speed of light. It would take an infinite amount of fuel to get the rocket ever closer to the speed of light, while at the same time the rocket becomes ever more massive. So, it is the rocket's mass that prevents it from ever fully reaching the speed of light. Only massless particles like photons can move at the speed of light, which is a velocity with no passage of time at all.[5]

Amazingly, this means that light literally exists outside the normal influence of time. A photon from a star can travel through space for billions of years without changing. Consequently, light energy exists in a realm having something of an eternal nature, displaying a God-like attribute. Light depicts what it means for God to be eternal, and living in a timeless state. As He said to Isaiah, "I am He; I am the first, and I am the last."[6] God is always in the present, and has all time before Him. He is, "I AM WHO I AM."[7]

Herein lies another paradox. The energy of a photon is related to its frequency of vibration, which is an oscillation in time. The higher its frequency of oscillation, the higher the photon's energy. Relativity tells us that no time passes for the photon, yet it oscillates and can interact with its physical environment, as when a photon is absorbed by an atom's electron. Energy oscillating and changing form without the passage of time is counterintuitive, but it happens countless times every second in the world of photons. In much the same way God is not confined by time.

Some Christian authors, as a way to prove a young Earth theory, claim that light has slowed down since the beginning of time. But there is no physical evidence to back this claim. In college, Stephen Hawking also thought light had changed since the beginning, but as a way to get to an eternal universe. He later revised his thinking saying, "I was sure there must be some other reason for the red shift. Maybe light got tired, and more red, on its way to us. An essentially unchanging and everlasting universe seemed so much more natural. It was only after about two years of Ph.D. research that I realized I had been wrong."[8]

Indeed, scripture says, "God is light and in Him is no darkness at all."[9] Now this does not suggest that the light energy in the universe is God, or a manifestation of God, but that pure massless light energy bears an image of God's purity, brilliance and His unchanging nature. As Jesus said, "God is Spirit, and those who worship Him must worship in spirit and truth."[10]

God's power is revealed in the harsh power of light from the Sun, which can bring both life and death. Intense solar radiation is, by itself, able to kill organisms and animals, and sterilize an entire planet. Yet life cannot exist without the right amount of light. Light therefore mirrors God's power over life and death. God's spiritual light reveals the real state of a person's heart, as Saint Paul wrote in Hebrews, "For the word of God is living and powerful, and sharper than any two-edged sword,"[11] cutting to the heart of every matter.

It should not be surprising that human eyes cannot see most wavelengths of light. Only a narrow range of the entire spectrum of electromagnetic radiation is visible. Our vision and understanding are necessarily limited, for we only register part of reality. Everyone has to believe in some things they cannot see.

Indeed, light has never been seen in its eternal like state. Light can only be "seen" during a process that involves an interaction of a photon with matter in a detector, or in an observer like us. Light is instantly converted from pure light energy into a higher energy state of an electron, inside a telescope's detector or in your eye's retina, then it is registered as a flash of light in the brain. We can "see" the effect of light in our mind's eye, but we don't see the photon itself, in the strictest sense. Likewise, as John wrote, "No one has seen God at any time. The only begotten Son, who is in the bosom of the Father, He has declared Him."[12]

GENERAL RELATIVITY AND GRAVITY

As we live within an ocean of light energy, we also live within an expansive gravitational field. Einstein's theory of General Relativity revised our description of gravitational interactions of bodies, like the Moon and the Earth. Gravity is now seen to be equivalent to a local curvature of space, imposed by large masses. Even massless light is seen to follow a curved path in space when it passes a massive star.[13] The gravity of a massive galaxy can act like a lens, focusing light from more distant galaxies for a favorably placed observer, just as Einstein predicted.

Einstein's curvatures must be taken into account when navigating a spacecraft to a planet. Being pulled into a planet's gravity field is to follow the curved space around the planet. A spacecraft in orbit follows the curvature of space around the Earth, in a balance between gravity's pull and the centrifugal force arising from the spacecraft's velocity. Gravity's influence over matter is inescapable, just like God's ultimate influence over all people, though they may wish to ignore Him.

QUANTUM MECHANICS

While relativity describes the way things behave on large scales, quantum mechanics describes the true interactions of the smallest particles and energy. Modern quantum theory came about as scientists sought to explain a few seemingly obscure phenomena, that were considered minor gaps in the classical scientific theories of the early 20th century. Quantum mechanics has since become absolutely foundational in the world of science. No one has ever reconciled the two theories, relativity and quantum mechanics, yet scientists and engineers use both theories routinely with great precision.

The name "quantum" derives from the fact that energy and matter cannot be subdivided beyond certain tiny quantized units. In other words, matter and energy come in discreet quantities on the smallest scales, rather than infinitely variable gradations. On the atomic scale of size, sharp edges disappear and boundaries become fuzzy wave-like things.

Einstein usually tops a list of the most influential persons, but in the end he spurned quantum mechanics, which he helped create. Ironically, quantum mechanics has been much more important to the modern technologies we take for granted, than the theory of relativity. For this reason, the unsung heroes of twentieth-century science are Niels Bohr, Max Planck, Paul Dirac, Werner Heisenberg, John Von Neumann, Erwin Schrödinger, and others.

Quantum mechanics made possible modern chemistry, including plastics, modern fibers, nano technology and materials of every sort, atomic energy, medical imaging, microbiology, telecommunications, cell phones, lasers, DVD players, digital cameras, modern electronics and computers. Quantum physics has even become essential to the study of space, by observing the oldest photons and the most powerful objects in space. Jane S. Dietrich says, "Cosmology and particle physics have come together... providing the 'laboratory' for high energies unattainable in earthly accelerators."[14]

Many people think that quantum mechanics is over their head, or boring, or not worth the time to learn. However, the men who worked out quantum physics struggled countless hours to theorize, calculate, and come to terms with its philosophical implications. It mattered a great deal to them what the physics implies about reality. Such was the struggle to come to terms with quantum physics that Bohr once told Heisenberg, "you must understand the torture I am putting myself through in order to get used to the mysticism of nature."[15]

It seems to me the importance of quantum mechanics to the Christian, in the current social climate, cannot be overestimated. Yes, quantum mechanics is complex and extremely mathematical. Fortunately, the overarching concepts of quantum mechanics can be grasped readily, if they are taken one simple step at a time. Quantum mechanics is the key to understanding God's deepest imprints in the universe. Ultimately, it will be difficult to counter science-based atheism without the support of quantum theory's implications.

However, most scientists today tend to ignore the implications of quantum physics, preferring to simply work with the equations.[16] I believe many of them do this because the quantum implications point so far away from the atheistic worldview. This may be why the latest crop of atheistic apostles is so angry. Quantum mechanics is an affront to the strictly material view of the world.

Quantum mechanics shows us how to think about the physical world. More than any other field of science, it reveals to us something of the mind of God.

Richard Feynman once told his university audience, "I hope you can accept Nature as She is—absurd. I'm going to have fun telling you about this absurdity, because I find it delightful. Please don't turn yourself off because you can't believe Nature is so strange. Just hear me out, and I hope you'll be as delighted as I am when we're through."[17] I too hope you will be delighted with quantum mechanics.

THE QUANTUM ATOM

The first great triumph of quantum mechanics was the quantum model of the atom, which is the basis of every material thing. The quantum model atom consists of neutrons and protons bound together by nuclear forces to form the atom's core, or nucleus. In complete atoms, tiny electrons orbit the nucleus.

The simplest, lightest atom is hydrogen. It has one proton and an electron only, while deuterium is a hydrogen atom that has a neutron added to form a heavier nucleus.[18] Each atomic element (material substance) has a different configuration of neutrons and protons in its nucleus, and each element has a unique mass. But in an electrically neutral atom, the number of negatively charged electrons always matches the number of positively charged protons. Electrically neutral atoms have a net electrical charge of zero.

Protons and neutrons are both relatively heavy, comprising 99% of an atom's mass within the nucleus. The electrons are ultra-lightweight particles spread out like waves, or a field around the atom's nucleus. Therefore, it is a misconception that atoms are mostly empty space.[19]

Protons and neutrons are composed of other more fundamental atomic particles called quarks, while electrons are fundamental particles in their own right. A fundamental particle is one that cannot be broken down into smaller constituent parts.

The neutron is unstable on its own. In spite of this, neutrons, when inside the nucleus, make complex atoms seemingly eternally stable. This makes possible molecules, or combinations of atoms. Without the neutron and its exact mass, nuclear force, and its electrical neutrality, there would be no material substance in the universe except hydrogen. There would be no stars, and no us.[20] The mass, electrical charge and inter-particle nuclear forces that bind the proton, neutron and electron also had to be balanced exactly for any matter to exist in the universe.

Stable atoms typically have the same number of neutrons, protons and electrons. The more neutrons and protons in the nucleus, the heavier is the element. For instance, sodium, nickel, iron and uranium are atoms in order of ascending mass.

Atoms with more neutrons than protons (isotopes) retain the same chemical properties, but some of these isotopes are not stable. Unstable atoms are radioactive, emitting one or more particles from the nucleus in a random fashion. This occurs by a process called quantum tunneling, and the escaped particles can register on a Geiger Counter. Quantum tunneling occurs when a particle escapes from an atom's nuclear binding energy, without having all the energy required to escape the binding energy 'barrier'. However, the timing of the escape is random, and there is only a small probability that a particle in any given atom will actually escape. Hence, the particle is said to 'tunnel' out through the energy barrier. Tunneling can happen when the particle's probability function of possible locations extends outside the energy barrier.[21]

A classical analogy would be that out of a thousand pebbles that are washed up against a dam one pops through the dam by chance without breaching it, and without having the kinetic energy necessary to penetrate the dam's wall. Of course, this cannot happen with pebbles and dams, but with tiny quantum particles tunneling does occur.

Tunneling takes place during fission in nuclear reactors, within the fuel of radioactive atoms. Transistors, the electrical component that made possible miniature radios and modern electronics, also rely on the miracle of quantum tunneling of electrons to function.[22]

Isaac Newton's classical formulas of mechanics are used to this day for most problems of motion and gravity. They also apply in my field of structural vibration. Newtonian mechanics, however, could not explain how an atom's electrons remained in stable orbits around the atomic nucleus. The attraction between the positive electrical charge of the proton and the negative charge of the electron should have caused every electron in the universe to spiral into its atomic nucleus, making chemical compounds impossible.

The problem of the stable atom was finally solved by the discreet (quantized) properties of the Bohr model of the atom, reflecting a sort of perfection of physical form that does not erode. Such a physical perfection does not exist on the size scale with which we are familiar—our cars rust, and things break down. But the quantum stability and function of atoms does not break down, reflecting the unchanging eternal perfection of the Creator.

In Bohr's quantum atom, electrons orbit the nucleus in discrete energy states, or shells, called orbitals. These orbitals are well defined energy states around the atom's nucleus. There are no gradations, or gradual changes, from one energy state to the next, but each energy state varies by a discrete amount. Electrons move between these energy states, these orbitals. When an electron absorbs a photon—a single packet of light—it goes to an orbital of a higher energy state. Later the same electron can emit a photon and jump back to a lower energy state or orbital.[23] The timing of these jumps is random.

No one has really seen an atom, but we know atoms exist. We know their structure and how they behave on the basis of repeatable physics measurements. In this way, atoms are a manifestation of God's unseen wisdom. It says in Proverbs, "(wisdom) was brought forth; while as yet He had not made the earth or the fields, or the primal dust of the world."[24] Atoms are that primal dust of the world that cannot be seen.

ELECTRICITY AND CHEMISTRY

We all have a passing familiarity with the atom's electron, since it is responsible for electricity. Electrons make your television, radio, automobile, and even your nervous system function. Today we take electricity for granted, but it took the quantum model of the atom to explain and exploit it.

In a suitable conductor, like a copper wire loop, electrons can be "stripped off" of their parent atoms when a voltage is applied to the loop. The voltage produces a massive flow of electrons within the copper wire, generating an electrical current. The electrons, neutrons, and protons in one atom are exactly like the electrons, neutrons, and protons in any other atom. This is another reason why electricity works; identical electrons can be traded endlessly among the atoms that make up the material of a conducting circuit.

The simplicity and complete interchangeability of such an innumerable quantity of electrons in the universe reveal something of the breadth of God's power, His awesome consistency, and the abundance of His provision. As it is written in Genesis 22 He is called "Yahweh Yireh", the Lord will provide —the God of more than enough.[25]

Static electricity is an accumulation of excess electrons on an object. They don't move as in a wire loop, but they simply collect and build up a voltage, or charge. If enough electrons collect on your finger, they will jump through the air to another conductor like a door knob, when the voltage potential is strong enough. Then you feel a sudden electrical shock with a snap. When a large static electrical charge accumulates on the Earth, a jagged lightning bolt flashes through the sky, powerful enough to disrupt your body's electrical functions, or split a tree open.

No one has ever seen an electron, proton or quark decay or change, but atoms do change, by combining with other atoms to form chemical compounds. Your body and everything you come into contact with is a collection of chemical compounds, of varying stabilities.

The quantum mechanical model of the atom describes the chemical reactions that atoms undergo (when atoms combine to form molecules) and it predicts the products of chemical reactions with high precision. For instance, one oxygen atom and two hydrogen atoms, both gases at ambient temperature and pressure, combine explosively to make a molecule of pure water. Chemists can calculate exactly the amount of water produced, as well as the amount of energy released in the chemical reaction. The same is true for all chemical compounds, so the success of the quantum mechanical model of the atom is complete.

The chemical bond strength between dissimilar atoms depends on their electron shell configurations. The electron shells link atoms together in chemical bonds that give each chemical compound unique material properties, mass, and chemical stability.

When atoms are aligned in regular crystal structures they form materials of high organization and strength. For example, iron has a lattice-like structure that is strong, but brittle. Steel is produced by adding certain other atoms like carbon or nickel at the right positions within the iron-crystal lattice, significantly increasing overall strength, ductility and corrosion resistance.

Science describes the atom and its behavior very well. However, no one but God knows how the perfection of the atom's components can exist, created out of nothing but radiant energy. The seemingly arbitrary and finely tuned rules, that dictate the atom's discrete form and function, give it stability and reveal the work of a dependable sustaining and organizing Mind. As is says in Proverbs 3:19, "The LORD by wisdom founded the earth; by understanding He established the heavens."[26] The apparent incorruptibility of the atom's proton, electron and quark components bear the likeness of God's unchanging eternal nature and purity.

Now let us dive deeper into the unseen underlying structure of the universe.

CHAPTER EIGHT

QUANTUM INSCRUTABILITY

"You do not know what is the way of the wind ...
So you do not know the works of God who makes everything."
~ Ecclesiastes 11:5 (NKJV)

Everyday common sense experience derives from the predictable movement and reactions of objects in space and time, like tennis ball trajectories, and cars moving along a freeway. Scientists refer to this as the Classical World, and its interactions depend on classical Newtonian physics. We develop a kind of faith in the dependable way the world works.

Eighteenth century philosophers inferred from Newton's laws of motion that if the initial states of all particles were known, then the outcome of all systems in the universe could, in principle, be predicted. Laplace championed this philosophy, called Determinism, and it implied that God created the universe and then spun it off to evolve in an absolutely predictable way.[1]

Determinism was a comforting idea to the materialists of the time, since it provided an entirely natural explanation that seemed to contain everything. On the scale of size that we humans experience, determinism seemed to be entirely correct. It also agreed with the Christian Calvinistic concept of strong predestination in which nothing occurs by chance but is predetermined by God. It was widely believed at the turn of the 20th century that science had already discovered everything of real importance, and that there were just a few nagging details to clear up.

Philosophers came to believe that determinism meant true free will was out of the question—that man was just a biological machine with no power to determine his or her own destiny. Many evolutionary biologists still see human beings this way. Ironically, a human that is just a biological machine could not engage in true rational thought, and science would not be possible.

Then in 1926, Werner Heisenberg made a startling discovery—a fundamental limit to the precision of measurements performed on small particles.[2] The new quantum uncertainty was fundamentally different from human ignorance of the fine details of a particle's trajectory, or its initial conditions. Heisenberg's uncertainty principle shook material determinism to its core, since the outcome of a physical process is not entirely predictable. That is, chance events are real.

Steven Hawking affirmed the inescapable truth of uncertainty and chance events saying, "This uncertainty principle of Heisenberg showed that one could not measure the state of a system exactly, so one could not predict exactly what it would do in the future. All one could do is predict the probabilities of different outcomes. It was this element of chance, or randomness, that so disturbed Einstein. He refused to believe that physical laws should not make a definite, unambiguous prediction for what would happen. But however one expresses it, all the evidence is that the quantum phenomenon and the uncertainty principle are unavoidable and that they occur in every branch of physics."[3]

Quantum physicist Nick Herbert unpacks the unsettling reality of uncertainty, "Bohr and Heisenberg can claim that, despite its statistical character, quantum theory gives a complete account of the facts. Critics, who object that this theory does not explain the observably different outcomes of electrons in the same state, fail to appreciate the nature of quantum randomness: identical situations give different results. That's all there is to it."[4] Quantum physics, then, describes the way things really are at small scales, and in a way that is irreconcilably at odds with strict determinism.

You know intuitively that the everyday world is not as predictable as idealized math models would indicate. The inherent complexity of mechanical design makes for uncertainty in aerospace engineering—you never know what might go wrong. This is why it is so important to test flight equipment for design flaws and workmanship faults. Materials can have cracks, material properties can be less than expected, adhesives can have the wrong mixture, or be expired, or they can be applied without proper surface cleaning.

Chance events are a cornerstone of quantum mechanics. Indeed, it is not really possible to understand the claims that atheists put at odds with Christianity without a clear understanding of chance events. Evolution is the foremost example. Atheists say that because evolution is driven by random events, design cannot be real, and there cannot be a Creator. What, then, are Christians to make of chance events?

DIVINE IMPLICATIONS OF UNCERTAINTY

Superficially, chance events don't seem compatible with a Creator, and many Christians believe that nothing happens by chance. But is this really the case? Jesus once said, "the wind blows where it likes,"[5] and He knew of which He spoke. Nature has been given a degree of free rein by God. It is impossible, even in principle, to predict what a quantum particle will do at any given moment.

This fact has a hugely important implication for us. If the human mind functions by the rules of quantum mechanics, then the behavior a person chooses cannot be predicted entirely. Yet our behavior is not random. We are aware of our choices, and we are free to act without being completely constrained by what has taken place before. Ergo, we have free will to choose.

Frank Tipler juxtaposes God's perfect knowledge and our free will as part of the fabric of reality, "God has constructed reality so that He can both know everything that can be known and yield free will for His creatures in this reality. The price of non trivial choices for we inhabitants of the universe—to accept one another and God, or not – is that nature can on occasion wreak havoc."[6] Jewish scientist Gerald Schroeder agrees, "Famines and holocausts do not occur because God is limited. ... God allows them to happen as part of the divine scheme. What seems to be divine indifference lies not in some inherent limit to the Creator. Rather it is the foundation of our free will."[7] Occasional calamity is the price we pay for free will.

God is certainly the author of freedom for all people because the root of freedom is inherent in the physics of the universe, through chance events. Free will and liberty must be of paramount importance to God since it also brings a great deal of trouble to Him and to us. Most significantly, freedom makes true love possible.

Most Christians have always believed in free will, as it is described in the Bible. Unfortunately, many Christians also accept the atheistic notion that chance events imply God's noninvolvement in nature, and so reject the idea of chance occurrences altogether. However, chance events are no more incompatible with Divine sovereignty than is free will. If you believe chance events are inconsistent with God's action in the world, how will you reconcile a person's willful disobedience with God's sovereignty?

The truth is more complex. The book of Ecclesiastes attests that chance is a biblical concept, when it says, "the race is not to the swift, nor the battle to the strong ... but time and chance happen to them all."[8] 2 Chronicles 18:33 says, "But a certain man drew his bow at random and struck the king of Israel between the scale armor and the breastplate."[9] Jesus also mentioned the concept of chance in the parable of the Good Samaritan, "by chance a certain priest came down that road. And when he saw him (the wounded man), he passed by on the other side."[10]

Determinists have argued for decades that quantum physics, with chance events, is an incomplete description of reality. Einstein once said that "God does not play dice," and I used to believe this, but something else entirely has been discovered. A strict deterministic view has been contradicted by decades of quantum physics experiments, repeated in laboratories around the world. It turns out that God controls the universe through physical laws that include random chance at the smallest scales. God has no need to control every random occurrence in the stream of time. He designed the universe to do that for Him.

The paradox is that He knows everything that will happen, even though some events are intrinsically unpredictable. What then of Divine predestination of events? Saint Paul wrote about the predestination of believers, showing how this works, "He chose us in Him before the foundation of the world, that we should be holy and blameless before Him. In love He predestined us for adoption as sons through Jesus Christ, according to the purpose of His will."[11] The predestination of events in the world works the same way.

It is God's eternal viewpoint outside time, His ability to see the beginning from the end, and not determinism, that gives Him this knowledge and control over random events. This is affirmed in Ephesians 2:10, "we are his workmanship, created in Christ Jesus for good works, which God prepared *beforehand*, that we should walk in them."[12] God's will was laid down before the foundation of the world, and does not necessarily depend on the outcome of tiny random events. God is the master scientist and analyst, yet He knows all things simply by seeing, in the same way we know by seeing. We are, after all, made in His image.

Essentially, chance events and God's sovereignty are compatible because God chose the outcome of as many random events as He desired, when He selected the initial states of the universe. This is why Darwinist arguments against design based on tiny, uncontrollable, random events are not correct. God's control of random events is largely from outside time—from before time began. He can also alter outcomes of random events in the stream of time without leaving a trace. We need a view of God who is big enough to deal with random events, and with people who have free will.

THE PROBLEM OF EVIL

We tend to see catastrophe and disease as a natural form of evil. There is a degree of randomness to the timing and severity of storms, earthquakes, volcanoes and other disasters. If the Earth had no molten core of iron, with its magnetic field there would be no earthquakes, but our atmosphere would soon be lost to solar radiation. God allows malaria, but every organism on the planet competes for resources, and some of those competing organisms just happen to be detrimental to us. If single-cell germs did not exist, neither would "good" cells. There would be no good gut bacteria, no blood cells, or immune system cells, or any of a host of other specialized cells that comprise our bodies. Without the various and competing cells, we would not be here. So to a degree, natural catastrophe is a matter of perspective.

Chance events, taken with the Bible, lead us to the familiar doctrine that God directly causes some events, but merely allows other things to happen. A scriptural example of this is the testing of Job, the Old Testament saint.[13] When Satan raised the challenge, God allowed Satan to test Job, who was an upright man. Yet the evils that befell Job did not come from God, but from Satan, and by the same latitude to do evil that God gives us. God did not cause Job's suffering, even though He knew from the beginning of time that Satan would test him. It is freedom for God's creatures that made Job's suffering possible, and Satan's animus that brought it about.

In Jesus' day, people thought that suffering and calamity meant that the sufferer had committed some great sin. Today, many people in the West believe suffering means God is bad, or is proof that He does not exist. How then did Jesus Christ view the ravages of chance evil events? There are two stories from the Bible that instruct us here.

The first instance is from the book of 1 Kings, when God told Elijah to stand on the mountain before the Lord. "And behold, the LORD passed by, and a great and strong wind tore into the mountains and broke the rocks in pieces before the LORD, but the LORD was not in the wind; and after the wind an earthquake, but the LORD was not in the earthquake; and after the earthquake a fire, but the LORD was not in the fire; and after the fire a still small voice."[14]

God was not in the wild random behavior of the wind, however fierce, or the earthquake, or the fire, but in a still small voice. He did choose the universe that set the wind, the earthquake, and the fire in motion, but they all unfolded by natural law. So it is that God is not in every random occurrence or evil that happens, and not every tribulation has a great meaning. However, God can, and does use anything that happens for the good of His people, though we may not understand presently why certain things befall us.[15]

The second story is from the book of Luke which recounts Jesus' view of senseless tragedy. A gathering of people told Jesus about some Galileans whom Pilate had murdered. Jesus replied saying, "Do you think that these Galileans were worse sinners than all the other Galileans, because they suffered in this way? No, I tell you; but unless you repent, you will all likewise perish.

Or those eighteen on whom the tower in Siloam fell and killed them: do you think that they were worse offenders than all the others who lived in Jerusalem? No, I tell you; but unless you repent, you will all likewise perish."[16]

Jesus recognized the tragic nature of the two deadly events, yet He did not focus on the misfortune of the victims as we would, and He didn't call for a safety commission. Rather, Jesus insists that we will all die tragically if we are not in a right relationship with God, with eternal consequences. So God's perspective of events is really quite different from ours.

In the beginning, God pronounced His created order to be very good, but He did not call the universe perfect. God commanded mankind to "subdue the earth" in Genesis 1:28. This indicates that effort was required to subject the created order to human purposes, that the Earth was untamed. We also know that pain existed in Eden. God told Eve in Genesis 3:16 (NASB), "I will greatly *multiply* your pain in childbirth."

I believe God created the world just as it is, with its beauty, joys, random events, entropy, suffering and pain. Every forensic detail from biology, paleontology and astronomy indicates this is so. So does the Bible. In His garden, God gave Adam a choice, to follow His instruction, or to rebel. God willed that evil was possible from the beginning. So, the issue boils down to this, if God created the world as it is, is He responsible for evil?

Secular critics would say yes, that God is not powerful, or worse yet, that He is malevolent. Otherwise, He would stop evil from occurring. In their minds, evil precludes the possibility of a powerful and good God. Quantum scientists readily accept paradoxical concepts like the dual nature of light. It can behave like a wave or particle. The existence of a good and powerful God, along side the existence of evil, is such a duality, however discordant it may seem. God's critics would like to have it both ways, not believing in God because He does not eliminate evil in the current age, yet saying that God is not good if He judges and destroys evil in hell.

Atheists also say that God can't be good and loving if He consigns His own creatures to hell. They insist that this reveals the illogical nature of the Christian concept of a loving God. An underlying assumption here is that evil is not real, and that people cannot really be bad, and should not go to hell. But to say God is 'bad' for sending creatures to hell is itself a value judgment that assumes the existence of evil, so this argument against God is confounded. On the other hand, if evil actually exists and if God's long term plan is to keep it out of His heavenly realm, restraining evil in an inescapable hell makes a great deal of sense.

Neither good nor evil have any meaning apart from God, if the universe is just an accident. The truth is, the physics of the universe have been so finely tuned, that our existence is scarcely possible. None of God's critics has any idea how to design a better universe than ours, let alone one without evil.

God has given us the responsibility to choose whether good or evil will occur in the world, as we choose our behavior. God says that we are free to choose our path in life, "I have set before you life and death, blessing and cursing; therefore choose life, that both you and your descendants may live."[17]

God is not responsible for the evil deeds of men. Job 34:12 says that God does no evil, and James 1:13 tells us that He does not tempt anyone. Christianity, as a Divine construct, should not be judged by people's poor behavior, for Jesus came to save imperfect people. God is aware of everything that humans do at some level, but He is not involved in what we do at the level of "cause". That He leaves to us.

Our free actions form a paradoxical complement to God's knowledge and casting of every event. The freedom to choose necessarily means we have the freedom to do both good and evil. In our universe it is possible to love God and our fellow man, or to hate both, and do all manner of evil deeds. Those who say God is the author of human evil are really transferring blame from man to God, for the things that men choose to do.

In order to eliminate moral evil from the here and now, God would have to deprive us of our choice for good or evil. But such a universe would be morally trivial, and real love would not be possible by any of His creatures. God created this universe with real choice, where love is possible, and evil is necessarily a counter moral choice. God's solution to evil follows a different arc from the one that atheists seem to insist upon, which would require a universe of automatons.

How, then, do we defend the goodness of God? Some Christians try to do this by assuming a perfect world at creation, that was corrupted by Adam's fall. The Bible does say that God created a perfect world. We know it as heaven, and despite Heaven's perfection, rebellion against God arose even there. To complicate matters, God knew beforehand that evil would arise in both heaven and on earth.

Patrick Franklin poses a few questions that expose the weakness of the 'perfect beginning' as an explanation for evil. If God plans to make His followers incorruptible in the future, why didn't He make us that way from the beginning, and avoid all the sin, pain and suffering? Why were Adam and Eve so seemingly ill equipped to resist temptation? And, why does Genesis make no attempt to get God off the hook for the existence of evil?[18] Theologian John MacArthur agrees, "Its not one of the inadequate short answers like, "Well, God's not responsible (for evil). Adam and Eve are."

MacArthur goes further in an unflinching look at the issue of evil, "We will never be able to divest God of the responsibility for the *existence* of evil. He allowed it and designed it into this universe without being responsible for it (evil acts)."[19] 1 Samual 2:6-8 declares, "The Lord kills and makes alive." Amos 3:6 says, "If there is calamity in a city, will not the Lord have done it?" God declared through the prophet Isaiah (45:5-6), "I am the Lord, and there is no other; there is no God besides Me.... I form the light and create darkness, I make peace and create calamity; I, the Lord, do all these things."[20] There are many such verses in the Bible.

MacArthur concludes, "Here is God taking full responsibility for the existence of evil, since He is God and He controls everything. Evil is no disruption in God's purpose. Evil exists, sovereign God exists. Inescapable is the third point, God wills evil to exist. ... You can't get God off the hook. "He allowed it (evil) and designed it into this universe without being responsible for evil acts."[21] This view is as old as the Bible itself.

Now the question is, why does God allow evil to exist? Certainly, we can say that God wants to love creatures in our kind of universe. A second answer comes from the Bible. Romans 3:5 declares that, "Our unrighteousness demonstrates the righteousness of God."[22] The Westminster Confession of 1646 amplifies this proposition, "God, from all eternity, did by the most wise and holy counsel of His own will, freely and unchangeably ordain whatsoever comes to pass. Yet so, as thereby neither is God the author of sin, nor is violence offered to the will of the creatures, nor is the liberty or contingency of second hand causes taken away.... All that God decrees and providentially brings to pass is all to the praise of His glory."[23] MacArthur sums up his thesis, "Therefore, the existence of evil is, in the end, to the praise of His glory.... God puts His righteousness on display in the way He confronts and deals with sin, and that becomes the very essence of heavenly worship."[24]

This worship is described in Revelation 15:1-3, "And I saw... those (saved by God) who have the victory over the beast, over his image and over his mark and over the number of his name, standing on the sea of glass, having harps of God. They sing,... "Great and marvelous are Your works, Lord God Almighty! Just and true are Your ways, O King of the saints! Who shall not fear You, O Lord, and glorify Your name? For You alone are holy."[24] God makes His glory evident by His contrast with evil, and by His complete control and ultimate victory over it.[25]

This reappraised reading of scripture accounts for the existence of evil, and why God allows it. It accounts for the fall of an historical Adam, humanity's sin state, and how sin was imputed to the world by the spread of Adam's law. All this was done without adding a word to scripture. There are no unresolvable theological issues related to an ancient universe, evolution, entropy, random events, or pain and suffering. It is clear that nothing in science or nature changes the Bible's message. But, the question remains, what is God's solution to evil for us?

A LIMIT ON KNOWLEDGE

The strangeness of the uncertainty principle and its implications for our faith only begin with chance events. The uncertainty principle limits the amount of knowledge that is possible to acquire in a peculiar way. Specifically, the uncertainty principle says that if the momentum of a particle is measured with high precision, knowledge of the particle's position at that same moment, is lost to us. Conversely, measuring the position of a particle precisely, eliminates the possibility of measuring its momentum.

This means, for instance, that if the position of an electron is identified as it hits the screen of your television, we can't be certain about its momentum, or path to the screen. It also means that initial conditions for a given particle can never be known with complete certainty.[26] This is one of the principle paradigm-shifting aspects of quantum physics.

Scientist Evan Walker explains how significantly Bohr's view of deep reality began to change with the uncertainty principle, "For Bohr, the uncertainty relationships were not just some inability to make accurate measurements but were the very stuff of reality."[27] But it was Heisenberg who deduced the eerie truth, that an electron's path does not exist as a real path until it is measured, but only as a probability function of all possible paths.[28]

Decades later, physicist Richard Feynman asserted that an electron takes all possible paths to its destination, which is another way of saying that an electron (or photon) has no particular path until a measurement is made.[29] This means that electrons and other quantum particles can be thought of as existing in a physical form of possibility.

There is an image that demonstrates what this means. In 1989, scientists succeeded in positioning individual Xenon atoms on a metal nickel surface, by using a scanning tunneling microscope.[30] The resulting image shows light gray, false color, mounds that spell out IBM.

More accurately, the mounds are actually probability clouds, inhabited by the 54 buzzing electrons around each Xenon atom's nucleus! The gray probability clouds have the shape of the famous Bell probability density curve, that teachers use for grading papers. Electrons are most likely to be where each mound is tallest. This image directly illustrates the physical reality of the probabilistic kind of existence that electrons have around the atom.

It is commonly believed that quantum uncertainty is merely a limitation of our measuring instruments, or that uncertainty arises only because a particle is "disturbed" by the measurement process. While it is true that measurement always disturbs an atom's state, the reality is deeper.[31] It is impossible to measure both momentum and position, on the subatomic scale, even in principle with perfect instruments.[32]

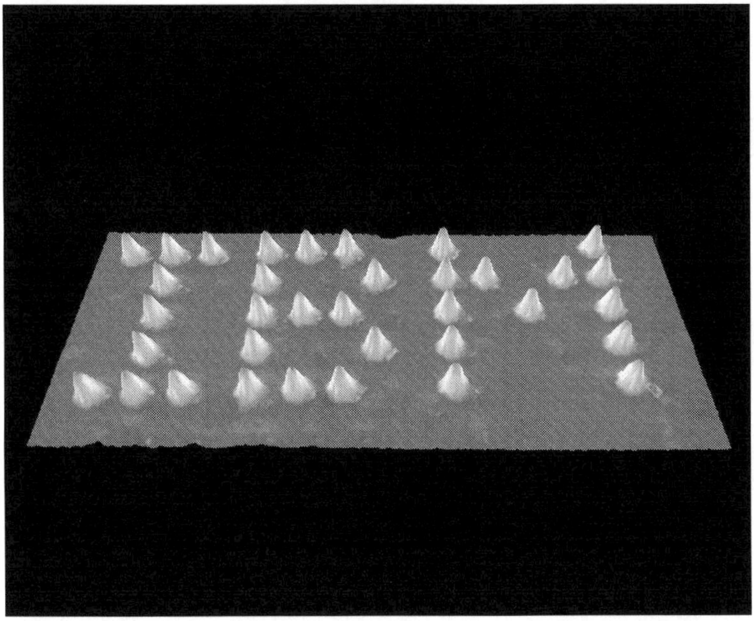

Scientists spelled out IBM with individual Xenon atoms on a metal nickel surface using a scanning tunneling microscope. The gray cone shaped 'probability functions' reveal the possible electron locations around the Xenon nuclei. Image originally created by IBM, Almaden Research Center

There is a unique type of measurement that refutes the measurement disturbance model of uncertainty. Consider a laboratory apparatus in which single photons can be made to travel one of two paths to a screen, path A or path B. There is no way to know which of the two paths any given photon will take, A or B. Then a photon detector is placed in path A, so that we will be alerted when a photon takes that path. Next, a photon is sent through the test setup and it strikes the screen, but the detector in path A does not click. We can deduce that the photon has gone down path B, so that information about the photon's path has been obtained without disturbing it. This demonstrates that the "disturbance" view of measurement is really a misstatement of the true physics.[33]

The uncertainty principle has ended human hope for a complete knowledge of the universe. Maybe things are not as predictable as we might have wished. It turns out, even a tennis ball's trajectory can't be exactly predicted, since the ball's mass, surface irregularities, and initial conditions always have a degree of uncertainty. In one sense, the uncertainty principle does mean accepting a level of non-definiteness in life, that seems antithetical to religion. Yet this feature of the human condition is accurately depicted throughout scripture. The uncertainty principle has not made God's existence or His action in the world less certain, but it has demolished the deterministic worldview that surmised God could be discarded.

Some Christians will object that the uncertainty principle puts a limit on God's knowledge. However, the orthodox Copenhagen interpretation of quantum physics says that to the extent a quantity is unknowable (unmeasurable) that quantity does not actually exist. God's knowledge and power cannot be required to include that which is logically impossible to know or do. Therefore, the Heisenberg uncertainty principle does not limit God's knowledge or His power.

THE EVERYDAY WORLD

You may wonder, how it can be that familiar consistent experiences come out of nature, if it behaves as the uncertainty principle says? Bohr's correspondence principle says the classical world of Newtonian physics is a special case of quantum physics.[34]

Schrödinger further explains why our experience seems so predictable, while occurrences in the quantum world are so foreign. First, he poses a question and then he answers it, "Why must our bodies be so large compared with the atom? ... if we were organisms so sensitive that a single atom, or even a few atoms, could make a perceptible impression on our senses— Heavens, what would life be like! ... An organism of that kind would most certainly not be capable of developing the kind of orderly thought which (human beings have)."[35] So, human experience is insulated from the quirky behavior of quantum particles by our physical size, and by the sheer number of atoms in our makeup.

MIRACLES AND UNCERTAINTY

Another curious phenomenon predicted by the Heisenberg uncertainty principle is that empty space is not really empty. Space is actually full of energy called the Zero Point Field. This energy has been demonstrated as a force exerted on smooth parallel plates, when they are spaced within a millimeter of each other. Quantum particle pressure waves between the plates cancel, and exert little outward pressure on the plates, so that the quantum particle pressure, outside the plates, pushes the plates together. Haisch suggests this energy field is a manifestation of God's ongoing process of creation, just as the Bible describes God's sustaining hand.[36]

Amazingly, the uncertainty principle is also the means for a class of events that contrast with chance occurrences—premeditated miracles. By the uncertainty principle, God may select the outcome of otherwise random events, without violating His own physics. Such Divine tampering would be essentially inscrutable, leaving no detectable trace for science to find, except for the observation of occurrences that are unlikely in the extreme, like the fine tuning of the constants of physics, the beginning of the universe, and the mechanisms of life.

Many Christian theologians, like St. Augustine, have for centuries taken the view that miracles do not violate physical law. In this tradition, miracles are unlikely events that bolster God's purposes and the Church's mission, but which don't break natural law.[37] Why would God change His word in nature—natural law—any more than He would countermand His written law? Both embody God's will. God has access to every physical law, and He has the power to perform what He wishes with those principles, and He knows them all, while we do not. He alone has the highest level of access to those laws.

Clearly, the creation of the universe defies standard physics, which cannot describe it. Miracles like the restoration of sight to the blind, or the resurrection of the dead are also of a different class than the merely "extremely unlikely" event. Something is being undone that is otherwise considered irreversible. God has the power to rebuild biological optical systems at the molecular level, by changing individual quantum states, but how exactly such miracles might be accomplished is conjecture. Jesus walking on the surface of the water is another miracle of an unknown mechanism. Such a feat would seem to require the projection of a force field of some kind, and one that would not overly disrupt the immediate surroundings, including the surface of the water. It has been proposed that miracles, like walking on water, might be powered by neutrino energy fields.[38]

One thing is clear, God's miracles are performed in this earthly physical realm, so they result in real physical outcomes with real matter and energy. It seems to me that the suspension of natural law is not a requirement for God to do miracles, but miracles do require an implementation of natural law by a means far beyond human ability.

Scripture backs the view that God chose ahead of time what interventions He would make in the world, to glorify Himself and make Himself known. God does not have to change His mind to 'change' the unfolding of history—to perform a miracle. When asked why a certain man was born blind, Jesus replied, "It is not that this man sinned, or his parents, but that the works of God might be displayed in him."[39] God planned the miracle of sight in that blind man in advance. He might choose any number of like signs.

The Bible tells us that our prayers can change things, when we ask for a miracle. It says in James 5:16, "The effective, fervent prayer of a righteous man avails much."[40] Prayer can transform human relationships, one's standing with God, and physical outcomes in the world. The fervent prayers, of even a single person can change history, as can be seen in the lives of David, Nehemiah, Daniel, Ester and Moses of the Bible. God still does miracles. I personally came to believe in God as a child through answers to simple and trusting prayers. Yet, we do not know if God will work a miracle in our circumstance until we ask.

GOD'S SOLUTION TO EVIL

We should not be surprised that the world is so complex, running along deterministic principles, and also with chance events. Accepting such a paradox requires something more than conventional linear reasoning. This is not irrationality, but it is a means of accepting the reality of physics, and the uncertain nature of the human condition.

There is evident a weak solution to evil in the world. I say this because human beings throughout history have struggled against evil, both corporately and individually, to attain to periods of peace and tranquility. Those who say military power and war solve nothing have not really considered how awful a world dominated by the Nazis, or the communists might have been, or how oppressive life under Islamic law would be. It is legitimate to expect that Christians should fight for freedom and country when necessary. The New Testament's only recorded instruction to soldiers was simple, "Do not extort money from anyone by threats or by false accusation, and be content with your wages."[41]

My point is that the West's struggle in World War II, and the cold war resulted in a relatively long period of general peace, at least in the Christianized West. That such temporal peace exists, and that we naturally pursue it, shows that good does have some ascendancy in our world. Moreover, most people are happiest in close loving relationships. So, the first hints that God has a solution to evil come from the states of human existence that most people prefer, peace and loving relationships. Rather than asking why evil exists, perhaps we should wonder why there is any good in the world, for all good comes from God.

So what is God's solution to evil for human beings? The honest observer would have to admit that God might have further plans for resolving evil, that are not immediately obvious. This is not something we can deduce from nature. We must have a Divine revelation in order to know God's intentions for dealing with evil. I believe this is what God has given us in the Bible and in Jesus Christ.

In a practical sense, Jesus Christ taught us how to respond to evil. We are to pray about all our anxieties, fears and concerns, and lean on Him. God promises to help us through every trial. He certainly prayed to protect His disciples when He said, "I do not pray that You should take them out of the world, but that You should keep them from the evil one."[42] We who are in Christ are His agents in the world, and we are to follow Him and grow to maturity, despite adversity. God can use our failures, emotional scars and struggles to help us grow, and enable us to help others that struggle in similar ways.

God does not want us to be hapless victims of chance or malicious evil, but St. Paul tells us, "Do not be overcome by evil, but overcome evil with good."[43] Psalm 31 admonishes us in the face of adversity, "Be of good courage, and He shall strengthen your heart, all you who hope in the LORD."[44]

Having said that, and despite a grounded knowledge of good and evil, I find that a part of me, on an emotional level, still does not understand the distress of suffering. At times I recoil from the paradox of God's beneficent control, moral evil and tragic chance events. It seems to me that it is impossible to rise above suffering completely, as exemplified by Jesus' prayerful anguish before His crucifixion.[45] We are too closely bound to suffering by our physicality.

Yet, we are not to be guided by our feelings, but by a reasoned faith in God's promises. Help comes when I release my concerns, sinful impulses, lack of faith, and my whole person to God without reservation. He understands us and He does not exempt Himself from our suffering or our tribulation, for He suffered as one of us in the person of Jesus Christ. We do not grow spiritually by our own effort, or by trying harder, but by putting on God's righteousness and power by praying the scriptures.

Ultimately, uncertainty and calamity are meant to remind us that our existence is transitory, that this world has an end, and that we are to seek God and trust Him alone. Only a right partnership with God, and a view to our eternal destination in Christ give us the proper frame of reference to view the evils that occur in the world. That eternal life came through Christ's suffering on the cross proves that God can bring good out of the greatest evil, as it says in Romans 8:28, "all things work together for good to those who love God, to those who are called according to His purpose."[46]

God's final answer to evil, then, hinges on His love and mercy, which He demonstrated in the sacrificial death of Christ. Jesus said of this, "Greater love hath no man than this, that a man lay down his life for his friends."[47] Jesus bore in His body a contradiction, subjecting Himself to the evils and brutalities of human nature, even as He gave Himself to save us.[48] He bore our inadequacies and our sin in the face of a perfect God, whose wrath He took in our place. Then He conquered death and evil in His resurrection, which means eternal life for anyone who can accept it.

Jesus encouraged us saying, "Rejoice that your names are written in heaven."[49] This is the final word on evil for those of us who know Him, those who are willfully entangled with Him. Because of this, I find I can accept life as it really is. I can face myself with the good and the bad, as I stand in the light of His love and sin covering. We can take courage in the hope of a glorious eternity with God. Because He has complete control over evil, we can trust that it will never intrude on our life in heaven.

The eternal destiny of a person who does not know God is uncertain. It is in a state of potential for great good and beauty, or for utter darkness and desolation. No one is exempt from these two possibilities. Many will not accept God's solution, and there is no final solution to evil for those who oppose God. They say this life is all there is, and they have already received their reward in full.

The uncertainty principle also means possibility, both for good and evil. The reality of human free will turns on the uncertainty principle and on random events described by quantum mechanics. Human choice is real, and we bear in our lives the consequences of our choices. Through our actions we become co-creators of the stream of history with God, so let us choose for the good.

CHAPTER NINE

A WORLD OF POSSIBILITY

"Where is the way to the dwelling of light, and where is the place of darkness, that you may take it to its territory and that you may discern the paths to its home?" ~ Job 38:19, 20, ESV

Light is pure energy and, curiously, as described by quantum physics, its behavior depends on its context. That is, light behaves differently depending on how it is measured. Light energy acts like a particle when a position measurement is made. Yet, the same light displays wave properties during measurements that detect waves. Light's particle and wave dual natures are called complementary properties, since they complement each other—they both exist—even as they seem to contradict each other.[1]

The same dual-natured behavior is true of any isolated quantum particle, like electrons, protons and neutrons, the building blocks of matter.[2] Material atoms also behave as waves or particles depending on the kind of experiment being performed. So the real nature of the solid stuff of life, the individual atoms of the chair you are sitting on, are as insubstantial as a wave, when they are isolated from other atoms. Collectively, the atoms add up to the "chair".

Actually, ordinary objects always display wave and solid particle characteristics. A ruler looks rigid until you brace it on a table edge and twang its free end, setting it to vibrate. Every material thing in the universe vibrates and transmits waves—the Sun, the Earth, the sound waves in a concert hall, even you. The difference being that the position and motion of classical objects like the ruler can both readily be measured and predicted, while only one of the two dynamic properties of a small particle—velocity or location—can be measured at a time. Furthermore, the location that a particle will have upon measurement is not entirely predictable, but is always just one of all the possible locations.

The dual nature of light is analogous to many of the other dualities we experience in life. We all struggle with the paradoxes of faith and doubt: good and evil; eternal life and earthly death; God's blessing in the face of earthly struggle; feeling joy and pain at the same moment. These things are superimposed in a way that transcends ordinary "either–or" reasoning—that is, beyond the paradigm of linear thinking.

Paul wrote about this kind of duality saying, "We are afflicted in every way, but not crushed; perplexed, but not driven to despair; persecuted, but not forsaken; struck down, but not destroyed."[3] Jesus Christ said, "For whoever would save his life will lose it, but whoever loses his life for my sake and the gospel's will save it."[4] Such paradoxes are not groundless Christian constructs; they are not so different from the paradoxical behavior of energy and fundamental particles.

This is not to say anything can be true just because you "see it as true", as some people claim. Even though light has a strange dual nature, there are many things that light cannot be made to do. For instance, light and matter do not behave like a featureless pudding that is infinitely divisible into smaller and smaller pieces. Nor is light transmitted in a medium like sound waves in the air. Instead, light's behavior follows the well defined equations of physics. Quantum physics describes a privileged physical truth, that transcends alternate views of reality. In this way, science exposes the folly of the postmodern view, that there is no real truth, or that one truth is as good as another.

Postmodernists say that since the behavior of a quantum particle depends on the type of measurement we choose, we are imposing preconceived notions onto the particle's behavior, thereby misinterpreting reality. Apologists of the modern multicultural doctrine gather some strength from such mistaken ideas.

So why would human beings impose concepts like wave, particle, position, and velocity on the poor tiny particles of the quantum world? We do this because quantum particles clearly display such properties and not others. While it is possible there may be other properties yet undiscovered, these are the standard ones. Wave, particle, position and velocity, energy, and time are the key parameters of classical mechanics that are observed in the interactions of even a few quantum particles. These are the parameters that are the foundation of our conscious experience. As I said, there is a privileged way of comprehending nature.

DESCRIBING POSSIBILITIES

In 1926, Erwin Schrödinger derived a wave equation that successfully describes the total energy of a particle, as it changes over time.[5] The wave equation can be interpreted as, "the probability that a particle is somewhere—a probability defined by what is called the particle's wave function, symbolized by the Greek letter psi (Ψ)."[6] In other words, the Schrödinger wave equation describes what may occur when a measurement is performed on a particle. It also holds for ensembles of particles.

The particles are constrained to manifest one of the possibilities described in the Schrödinger equation. The possible outcomes in the wave equation are deterministic, in that they can be described exactly. However, random chance determines which of the possible outcomes will actually happen in a quantum mechanics experiment. When an outcome has been selected, the wave equation is said to "collapse" to just one of the possible outcomes.[7] This is also referred to as the "state vector collapse", simply meaning that an outcome has been selected by nature—something happens.

The orthodox Copenhagen interpretation of the wave function is that something like probability is the true state of unmeasured particles.[8] This is like the mound shaped Xenon atoms that spelled out IBM, which were shaped by probability. Schrödinger's equation represents waves of possibility that a system may actually assume upon measurement. Existence in a realm of possibility is like a coin tumbling through the air, being neither heads nor tails. A measurement occurs when the coin lands on your palm and displays a head or a tail. Until a measurement is made, a particle's position and momentum exist only as a set of possible outcomes, a superposition of states like adding waves, and almost as insubstantial.

Quantum wave addition works the same way that waves do in water. When two waves of equal height come together, they add to make a wave twice as high as either one, and when a wave peak and an equal wave trough meet they cancel, and the water height returns to its undisturbed height. It is the same with waves of light or electrons. In quantum physics, matter particles also behave like waves, that can add and cancel each other just like energy waves. For this insight, Louis de Broglie received the Nobel Prize.[9]

The "collapse" of the wave equation may even be the key to the unidirectional passage of time—its forward direction. The selection of a single outcome, from the array of possibilities in the wave equation, might be what makes time move forward irreversibly.[10] The entropy of a system would increase by this process.

For sure, time's forward arrow gives us an orderly sense of reality, since it is not possible for the human mind to experience the events of all time at once, as it is for God. The forward movement of time is a requisite for us to be human and to experience life, to change, and grow. God on the other hand does not change. God desires that we remember His deeds of the past, to inform our current decisions, and that we forgive people for the wrongs we have suffered in days gone by. He wants us to exercise faith in Him and love Him in the present, and to love others as we love ourselves. We have hope in regards to His provision for us in the future.

PARADIGM AJAR IN JAPAN

My first experience on a space science mission to planet Earth was the NASA Scatterometer (NSCAT). It flew into space on a Japanese spacecraft named ADEOS (Advanced Earth Observing Satellite) sporting a suite of long stick antennas. ADEOS was a very large spacecraft, that was impressive to stand beside. It had a strange kind of beauty with its many electronics boxes and facets, all covered in real gold thermal insulation.

The NSCAT instrument was designed to measure ocean surface winds to facilitate the prediction of regional weather patterns and global climate. In 1995 I had the chance to visit the Japanese Space Agency in Tsukuba Japan, Science City. I was there for twelve days to observe the ADEOS spacecraft acoustic test, and monitor the safety of our NASA Scatterometer instrument during the test. At that time the Japanese space agency was known by the acronym NASDA.

Knowing that the Japanese revere their elders, I was amazed at the youthfulness of the crew working on the ADEOS spacecraft, and the sheer number of workers. Clearly, this increased their labor costs, but it fostered training and a group consensus that is significantly more important in Japan than in the United States. Most every Japanese person working at NASDA wore a colored uniform with their company logo, the uniform's color also identifying one's affiliation. MELCO (Mitsubishi Electric) ran the integration and test operation for the ADEOS spacecraft.

I kept myself apprised of the test activity progress through Mr. Ito, MELCO's integration and test manager for ADEOS. The first several days Mr. Ito seemed to sweat bullets whenever he talked to me. I think he was anxious about saying something improperly that would embarrass himself, or MELCO. But, after about a week he was not as anxious talking to me and he became less cooperative. He finally told me, "Not give data," in response to my request for information. In the end, Mr. Ito gave me a paper copy of the spacecraft acoustic test data, but only after I spoke with Mr. Kuramasu, a NASDA manager, and his boss.

By contrast, Mr. Kuramasu was an extremely pleasant man, astute and comparatively easy to talk to, his English being very good. Mr. Kuramasu was happy to offer me the acoustic test data I needed to do my job. We spoke for a half hour about our country's space programs. He told me that there were only 1,000 NASDA people in all of Japan, and that they managed all of Japan's space efforts. He said that NASDA's space budget grew modestly every year, and that they had their own sizable H-2 launch vehicle. He was proud of Japan's contribution to NASA's International Space Station project, a science module which was the largest single section of the space station.

In my spare time, I kept a journal of my paradigm jarring experiences in Japan. I was fascinated by the Japanese, their respect for one another and for me. I never felt hostility from a stranger, but I was keenly aware that I would forever be an outsider in Japan. At the same time, I reread a book by Hugh Ross that aimed to reconcile science and Genesis. His writing encouraged me that the creation account in the Bible is actually much closer to science than is commonly believed.

A couple of days after the acoustic test was completed, I attended a post acoustic test briefing in the NASDA test control room. I only understood the word 'spacecraft' during the entire hour long meeting. Still, I felt it important to make an appearance for JPL, since I traveled so far to witness the test activities. Tables were arranged in a square and there were about 20 men and two women there, several of whom did not speak, but they all remained attentive. Discussions appeared to be frank, and one or two men spoke about issues they seemed to feel strongly about. Then suddenly, the entire group stood and bowed in unison to conclude the meeting, and the acoustic test program. I startled and nearly fell off of my chair. The next day I was glad to be heading back to my family, and my familiar existence in the states.

The ADEOS spacecraft was launched into Earth orbit in 1996. In a heavy blow to NASA and Japan, NSCAT was lost after 9 months in orbit, when the ADEOS spacecraft failed. The problem was traced to the spacecraft's solar arrays.

The SeaWinds instrument was designed to take the place of NSCAT on a second Japanese spacecraft, ADEOS II. During its development, a SeaWinds carbon fiber antenna waveguide broke right in front of my eyes twice during sine vibration testing. The waveguide was simply glued back together, reinforced with doublers, and vibration tested twice more until it passed its test.

Then incredibly, the finished SeaWinds instrument was also lost, when a second spacecraft power failure put an end to the ADEOS II mission after just 10 months. The twin failures, on the back of the loss of Mars Observer, made me wonder what in the universe I was doing in the space business.

ONE UNIVERSE, OR MANY UNIVERSES?

There is a "many worlds" interpretation of the Schrödinger wave equation that says all the possibilities given by the equation actually exist, in a nearly infinite set of parallel universes.[11] The many universes taken together are called the multiverse. In this view, all possible states for the 10^{90}

elementary particles in our universe (10 followed by 90 zeros) actually exist in the multiverse. Multiverse adherents say this would result in 10^{500} different universes, an enormous number. However, there is no way to know in which universe (inside the multiverse) any particular outcome might occur.[12]

In the multiverse, every type of universe that could exist by the rules of quantum physics would, in fact, exist. In many of those universes, there would be another version of you, along with every possible genetic variation of every other human being and creature. These other "you" persons—each one in a different universe—would eventually do everything and make every choice that is possible for a you to make. A priori, there is no reason to think ours is the only universe, or even the first one that God has created.

The multiverse idea has been popularized in science fiction, like the Star Trek television show. Typically, a good Captain Kirk and a bad Captain Kirk, from different parallel universes, might change places, or even meet each other. The many worlds interpretation makes for enjoyable science fiction, but it is hard for me to take seriously.

In the multiverse, some of the various "me" persons would be thoroughly rotten, and some of me would be good. I know I have possibilities within me for great evil and great good, just like everyone else. But, the idea that I would make all possible choices in the universes, in which I could exist, would seem to make void my struggle to make moral choices before God. All the "me's" would eventually make all possible choices. Even more dubiously, the multiverse scenario implies that at least one of me might be morally perfect, strictly by chance, which is a proposition that I don't accept. Saint Paul wrote about this saying, "I have the desire to do what is good, but I cannot carry it out," because he saw that no human being can reach moral perfection.[13]

Such a massive set of universes does have one philosophical attraction. The multiverse creates every possible kind of creature on which God can shower His love, across the set of all possible universes. Tipler recalls that "The historian of ideas, Arthur O. Lovejoy has pointed out that theologians of centuries past drew another conclusion about the creative implications of God's love: not only did He create some creatures, but He created all possible creatures that could fit in the universe. To have done anything less would have meant that His love would lack a possible recipient, and God would not rest until all possible recipients of His love had been created."[14] God loves creatures in our kind of universe, as well as those in His heaven.

There may indeed be other universes. But I think there is only one of me, and that my struggle to make choices for good are non-trivial in the grand scheme of things. The Bible certainly indicates that God is very interested in our moral choices, and that we should choose the best course through life that we can.

All the physical evidence indicates that ours is a closed universe, meaning that information from these other universes, if they exist, will forever be inaccessible to us. No information can come to us from an outside universe or from another version of ourselves.[15] Since it is not possible for any human to find out anything about other universes in the multiverse, these other universes lose their physical meaning for us. In other words, the many-worlds interpretation of quantum physics is physically equivalent to the Copenhagen interpretation of wave potentialities. The Copenhagen interpretation is the one that I accept, because it matches the way the world works, and because of its implications regarding our conscious experience, as we will see later.

Many atheists believe in the multiverse because they think it sidesteps a Creator. It is generally agreed among scientists that the likelihood of creating a universe that leads to human beings strictly by chance is vanishingly small. They assume that if there are enough universes this problem is overcome, but they can't know this. It seems to me, it is more likely that impossibility in any given universe, summed over all the universes in the multiverse, still yields impossibility rather than certitude.[16]

Besides, the multiverse does not really restore determinism, or locality in physics, which is one of the main points of the idea. The direct action of forces on objects as the only means of bringing about a reaction is referred to as locality. Locality is like two billiard balls that strike each other, and in the process transfer energy and information. In this version of the multiverse, every quantum event leads to a new set of separate universes where all the physical possibilities actually occur. This is taken to restore determinism over the set of universes, and restore, in a global way, the common sense notion of physical forces that directly influence material particles.

But Herbert concludes of the multiverse that, “any model of reality in which a tiny event in the Andromeda galaxy can instantly split my reality into thousands of Xerox copies cannot, by any stretch of the imagination, be called ‘local’.”[17] Instead, the simple truth is that quantum particles do behave in a non-local fashion; they can be influenced without direct physical contact.

In Hawking’s multiverse, each universe is spontaneously created with a unique set of physical laws that are randomly generated.[18] Each universe is supposed to come into existence by a process described by M-theory, which depends upon the existence of Supersymmetry.[19] Supersymmetry is a theory that posits the existence of particles that are cousins of the elementary particles we currently know. It is likely, however, that Supersymmetry will have to be abandoned, due to lack of evidence. No such particles have been found even in the world’s largest particle colliders, casting Hawking’s self-generating universes in doubt.[20]

Personally, I think it strains credulity to believe in 10^{500} universes just to make it possible to have this one universe without God, by chance. But a multiverse does not actually bypass God. Even for a multiverse with no boundary in time, God is still there. Doctor Tipler points out that God is the sum of all “causes” even if the list of causes is infinitely long.[21] Analogously, an infinite number of terms can be summed to a finite answer using calculus.

Indeed, observational evidence has revealed the Initial Singularity as the first cause of the universe. Materialists say the Creator cannot be detected in experimentation and therefore should be dismissed. But the initial singularity that led to the Big Bang is no more detectable than God. In fact, the initial singularity can be taken as His intersection with the universe. Atheistic scientists argue that there is no physical evidence for God, but this should not be surprising. The material universe came out of that which is essentially non material (not describable by physics) and is outside time and space—the Initial Singularity.

The facts of the beginning seem to be closed to us forever, so we are left to decide on the evidence for ourselves, whether we will believe God, or not. The truth is, atheists ignore a multitude of Divine implications from their own science.

Multiple universes might answer the question of what God did before we came along—prior to 13.7 billion years ago—though such a question would seem to be a non-sequitur for the Super Being outside time and space. Either way, it has pleased God to create a staggering set of possibilities in this universe, and an unimaginable number of creatures on whom to shower His love. There could even be countless beings on different worlds in this universe that experience His love.

It would be just like God to create a universe with so much possibility, with all the possible quantum states for the 10^{90} elementary particles in the universe. Only He could formulate the wave equation for such a universe. It would be just like the God of Abraham and Moses to create so many creatures on whom to bestow His love, to create a universe that is more than mere matter, one that is full of potential— potential that can be quantified and realized.

CHAPTER TEN

THE MEASURE OF REALITY

"A full and fair measure you shall have, that your days may be long in the land that the LORD your God is giving you"
~ Deuteronomy 25:15

Observation is famous for bringing about an outcome in quantum physics. It is not so widely recognized that the same principle works in our daily lives, and for the same reasons.

It says in Proverbs, "Observe carefully what is before you,"[1] so the astute person is instructed to observe and act with wisdom based on the information gathered. In fact, everything we do follows the pattern of observing, choosing, and then acting. More than this, God wants us to be honest in our observations and actions, to be fair in our dealings with other people, and use truth in measurement.[2] Indeed, progress in science, commerce, and all human affairs depends on accurate and honest measurements, and integrity in reporting what we observe.

The simple act of observation is very deeply rooted in the fabric of reality. In our universe, the larger set of possibilities described by the Schrödinger wave equation eventually expresses itself in an outcome. The only question is, which possible outcome is the one that really happens in the world? To find out, one has to look—make an observation, which is, to make a measurement. Intriguingly, unexpectedly, such a seemingly simple thing as observation changes everything, when it comes to fundamental physics.

Indeed, the uncertainty principle and the Schrödinger wave equation together have imposed a broad sense of indeterminacy in science called the "measurement problem." It has long vexed philosophers. Objective reality would say that a particle has a real location and velocity, even if you don't "look," or measure those parameters. In quantum mechanics things are very different. Heisenberg says that a quantum particle's dynamic properties of momentum and position, basic to classical mechanics, as in the trajectory of a cannon ball, don't really exist on the smallest scales until a measurement is made.[3]

The measurement problem of quantum mechanics has been whimsically posed in jokes like, "If a man says something in the forest and there is no woman to hear, is the man still wrong?" Yet amazingly, eight decades of quantum experiments back Heisenberg's orthodox interpretation of the Schrödinger wave equation: that a photon, or electron, or an atom, in isolation has no definite location or velocity until a measurement is made.[4] The fuzzy substratum of physical reality is not something that anyone would have guessed. The role of observation in triggering an outcome is even harder for many people to accept, though there is abundant scientific evidence.

Measurement on the smallest scales causes a transformation from quantum potential—potentia, an information-like state—to the classical reality of position or momentum. Potentia, or the potential for an outcome, is said to be the true state of unmeasured particles. Herbert says, "Measurement, in Heisenberg's duplex world, is the sudden transformation of potentia into actuality."[5] In quantum mechanics, the nature of deep reality seems therefore to almost disappear until a measurement is made.

This is exactly what Roger Penrose was talking about when he wrote, "The more we understand about the physical world, and the deeper we probe into the laws of nature, the more it seems as though the physical world almost evaporates and we are left only with mathematics."[6] But the most incredible feature of the new physics is a bombshell.

ENCOUNTERING CONSCIOUSNESS

The Copenhagen interpretation of quantum physics leads to the conclusion that the act of observation is an integral feature of the physical measurement process of any quantum particle. A measurement performed by an observer, in a quantum experiment, causes all the possibilities of the Schrödinger wave function to "collapse" to a single outcome.[7] Heisenberg said of this, "a complete separation of the observer from the phenomenon to be observed is no longer possible."[8] Rosenblum and Kuttner wrote that John Von Neumann demonstrated, "that if quantum mechanics applies universally—as claimed—an ultimate encounter with consciousness is inevitable."[9]

Evan Walker concludes that, "this revised view of reality, in which we see the observer and consciousness as central to reality itself, is as significant as if we had found the key to the soul. Perhaps that is what has been found here."[10] Measurement and consciousness are found to be a deep part of reality, and strong objective reality disappears in the quantum realm. The role of the observer in quantum physics is surely one of the most amazing implications in all science.

You may wonder if the deep nature of physicality can really be that ethereal and strange. As someone has asked, "is the moon really there, if no one looks to see?" The apparent power of the observer has led some to say, erroneously, that things don't really exist until they are measured, or even that reality is whatever we want it to be. Well, quantum physics does not deny the reality of our experience; it is the basis of it. And yes, the moon is really there, even if no one is looking. Matter and energy really do exist in a physical form of possibility (potentia) even when an observation has not yet been made.

Nature always follows the predictable outcomes of the Schrödinger wave equation. What the Copenhagen interpretation of quantum mechanics does do is introduce a kind of observer mysticism into physics that is distasteful to many scientists, and especially to atheists. Materialists have been trying to overturn this feature of quantum mechanics from the very beginning.

Heisenberg relates that, "all the opponents of the Copenhagen interpretation do agree on one point. It would, in their view, be desirable to return to the reality concept of classical physics or, to use a more general philosophic term, to the ontology of materialism."[11] That is, opponents want to eliminate the role of the observer and reinstate determinism. It is no surprise, then, that ranks of atheistic scientists don't believe in the quantum power of the observer, or the implications that derive from it.

ENGINEERING OBSERVATIONS

By the time I was considered JPL key staff, Ball Aerospace in Boulder Colorado was one of my favorite companies to visit. I went there many times for meetings, and four major system vibration and acoustic test campaigns. It was a much easier trip than the east coast, and the projects were smaller and more varied. These included the Deep Impact comet explorer, the CloudSat Earth orbiting spacecraft, the HiRise telescope for the Mars Reconnaissance Orbiter (MRO), and the Kepler planet finding telescope. My purpose was to oversee the spacecraft contractor's vibration test programs, and assist them during testing. It was about this time that I began thinking seriously about consciousness for this book.

The beautiful angular Flat Iron mountains overlook the pleasant city of Boulder and its many good eateries. The microbrewery trend was in full swing and the Walnut brewery had some of the best beer and food in town. The Ball engineers were the easiest to work with too, their processes being the most like ours at JPL.

System vibration tests were best if they were boring, meaning nothing went wrong. Typically, by the time all the assemblies and subsystems were assembled into a spacecraft, they were so well tested that a boring test was the expectation of the project office. I don't mean to say that vibration tests, especially system tests, were easy or routine. It took a great deal of careful work, preparation, monitoring and thinking on one's feet to make a vibration test of a unique "one of a kind" spacecraft look easy. But system tests normally went well for us.

It was when something did not go as expected, or when a failure occurred, that a test crew received the most intense project scrutiny. Once during a system vibration test, a hand held calculator was accidentally dropped on a shaker computer control keyboard, and the computer imposed an unexpected second load pulse on the flight spacecraft. No damage was done, but the review process that followed led to many extra work hours for the team, and a significant amount of paper work. Unusual, but relatively benign problems like this were not uncommon during a vibration test campaign.

Ball Aerospace had no dedicated acoustic test chamber like JPL's. Therefore, acoustic tests were performed by placing a spacecraft in the center of a circular bank of massive concert speakers. Then the speakers were used to generate high intensity noise, to simulate the rocket launch and its attending spacecraft vibrations.

The Ball Kepler team was having trouble achieving the required acoustic test level with this speaker setup. They wanted to tear down the test setup and recalibrate the speakers; a lengthy process consuming up to two days. As an alternative, I suggested moving one bank of speakers closer to the spacecraft where the sound was too low, and we discussed a specific distance from the spacecraft to achieve the desired test level. Doing this raised the acoustic input just enough to meet the Kepler launch acoustics test specification. Then the full level test was completed with a minimum of lost time and expense.

THE BASIS OF MENTALITY

There is good reason why the role of the observer has only been recently discovered. It is actually quite difficult, experimentally, to make quantum particles exhibit their strange quantum behavior.

Hideo Mabuchi, of Cal Tech, describes the theory of quantum decoherence that explains why this is so. "Decoherence theory tells us that, when we take lots of tiny quantum parts and connect them together in a general way, we can pretty much expect to get a classical whole out of them."[12] When quantum particles bump together, somehow they lose their quantum strange behavior and naturally transition together to "normal" material behavior. This is how the familiar classical world emerges from the quantum world. We experience a stream of particular events—predictable events—rather than all possible events occurring at once.

This means the universe is designed for state selection, and not for a permanent ambiguity of position or velocity (or quantum state). The moon, rocky and solid, really is there, even when no one is looking. This fact runs counter to the postmodern penchant for indeterminacy, that conclusions are merely social constructs based on one's experience and group consensus.

Decoherence seems, at first glance, to eliminate the conundrum of measurement and the observer, but there is still something mysterious behind decoherence and state selection.

Scientist Roger Penrose believes that quantum particles bumping together is equivalent to making a measurement, because there is a protomentality associated with every quantum interaction. He says, "Although I had not explicitly asserted, in either Emperor or Shadows, the need for mentality to be 'ontologically fundamental in the Universe', I think that something of this nature is indeed necessary. No doubt there is some kind of protomentality; associated with every occurrence of (the collapse of the wave function), according to my own view, but it would have to be exceedingly 'tiny' in some appropriate sense."[13]

Physicist Freeman Dyson expressed the same idea; "It appears that mind, as manifested by the capacity to make choices, is to some extent inherent in every atom."[14] Other scientists are also convinced of this very thing.[15] This is not to say that tiny particles are conscious themselves, but that quantum particles interact with their environment in a knowing way, in a very real sense. The thought is that the capacity for consciousness seems to be 'built in' to physics.

Groups of atoms display a collective protomentality in the case of radioactive decay, as measured by a Geiger counter. Alpha particles escape spontaneously from the nuclei of heavy radioactive atoms, in a phenomenon called quantum tunneling. The escaping particles cause a Geiger counter to register the decay event by clicking. The probability that an alpha particle will spontaneously emerge from a nucleus depends on the half life of the radioactive material, each radioactive material having a different decay rate. Strangely, the atoms of a given mass of material seem to cooperate in the rate of radioactive decay.

This has prompted Gerald Schroeder to ask, "Are the individual atoms aware of how many have already decayed and so how many must decay today? Or more generally stated, is matter in some sense aware of its environment? It often seems so."[16] The evidence for the existence of the quantum protomentality is circumstantial, but it is extremely compelling.[17]

The Penrose protomentality calls to mind what Jesus said on His triumphal entry into Jerusalem, "I tell you, if these (people) were silent, the very stones would cry out."[18] Later, St. Paul wrote, "the whole creation groans and suffers,"[19] and in the same vein, David wrote, "Praise Him, sun and moon; Praise Him, all you stars of light,"[20] and again, "Let heaven and earth praise Him, the seas and everything that moves in them."[21]

I used to take these passages as strictly poetic in nature, but the revelations of quantum physics indicate that a more literal interpretation is called for. These strange sounding statements of the Bible speak to a certain level of awareness in inanimate objects, rooted in the basic physics of the material world. Essentially, these verses say that the material of the universe praises God, just by being what God made it to be.

UBIQUITOUS QUANTUM MEASUREMENTS

Quantum measurements are all around us if we know where to look. In biology, organisms with eyes see because of quantum mechanical effects within the eye and the nervous system. Biological visual systems are so sensitive, in some animals, that the tiny light flash of a single photon (or packet of light) can be detected in a dark room.[22]

The lasers in store checkout scanners, and in CD and DVD players, operate on quantum mechanical principles. Laser is short for Light Amplification by Stimulated Emission of Radiation, which is a complicated way of saying that the waves of light emitted from a diode are made to reinforce each other, forming a coherent beam of light. Coherent means the light waves are identical in direction, frequency, phase, and polarization, with the resulting light beam being extremely intense, and highly concentrated. A laser light beam does not spread out in the same way a beam from a flashlight does; it remains a tightly focused beam over great distances. These properties make lasers useful for encoding and decoding information, as in computer optical drives and DVD players. With sufficiently high energy, lasers can cut materials precisely, or burn through armor and shoot down missiles.

Beam splitters are another very common quantum apparatus. A beam splitter is a piece of glass, or crystal, that reflects a percentage of the incident photons, and transmits the rest. This may sound a little like magic, but even the windows in your home do this. This is why you can see a faint reflection of yourself in a window.

Most of the light passes through a glass plate, but a few percent of the photons reflect back, producing a "ghost" image. Such ghost reflections cause no end of problems in manufacturing camera lenses, and expensive lens coatings are applied to reduce this extraneous reflection. There is not a good model for partial reflection from glass, except to calculate the probabilities of transmission and reflection. The proportion of photons that reflect from a glass plate can vary between zero and 16 percent, depending on the thickness of the glass.[23]

Clegg marvels at partial reflection, "If the glass is the right thickness, (photons) will somehow know how thick the glass is at the point they hit the inside surface of the window, and instead of reflecting back, they will carry on through. Strange indeed."[24] Amazingly, light senses how thick a glass plate is, the instant it comes into contact with its surface.

TWO SLITS AND A SCREEN

The quintessential quantum physics experiment, and one of the most revealing, is Thomas Young's two slit experiment, first performed in the early 19th century.[25] Light is made to pass through two slits in a plate, and is projected onto a screen. In the figure that follows, red light passes through the two slits and produces an interference pattern on the screen. Where the red light waves add, there are red bands on the screen; and where the light waves cancel, there is no red on the screen. This convinced Young that light behaved only as waves.

But with modern equipment single photons can be sent through the slits one at a time. Astonishingly, a single photon interferes with itself, when passing through the slits in the plate. As the individual photons accumulate on the screen, they create the same colored and uncolored interference pattern on the screen that a stream of light would produce. Each photon goes through both slits at once, being in two places at one time. It is not possible to see a photon going through two slits at once, but this fact is implied by the wave interference seen in the experiment.

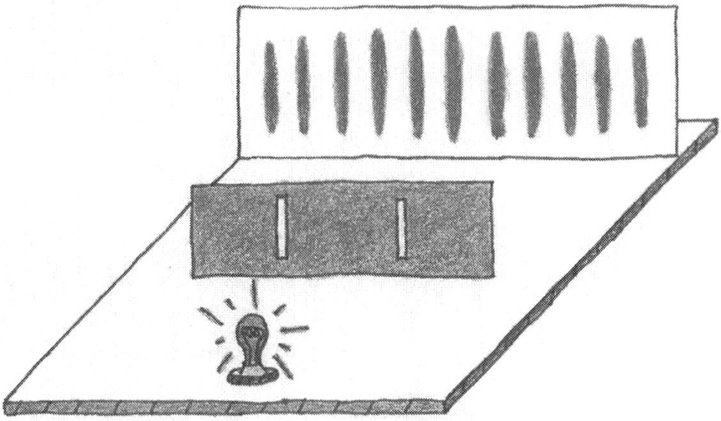

Young's famous two slit experiment is illustrated here. Photons go through both slits at once like waves. Wave interference creates red (gray here) light bands on the screen where the light waves add, but no red light is present where the waves have canceled.

If a photon detector is added to the setup, behind one of the two slits, say at the right hand slit, it will show when a photon goes through the right slit. However, it lets the photon continue on to the screen after detection. But something strange occurs. The mere presence of the detector at one slit constrains every photon to go through one slit, or the other, and the interference pattern on the screen disappears. Light passes through each slit independently, and the light forms two red lobes as though each photon was a tiny particle of energy. The wave property of light and wave interference have disappeared, each photon acting as a tiny discrete particle.

If the detector is switched off, the interference pattern returns. The wave interference pattern only forms on the screen when light goes through the slits undetected.[26]

When a light detector is placed behind one slit, the interference pattern suddenly disappears. Measurement has constrained every photon to pass through one slit, or the other. The result is that two diffuse lobes of red light (gray here) are created on the screen, each directly in line with a slit.

Most scientists take these facts at face value without thinking very much about the implications, but Schroeder exclaims, "Not only do the particles (or photons) know if the second slit is open, they know if someone is looking over their shoulders with a detector!"[27] There is the Penrose protomentality again.

Seth Lloyd also marvels at the outcome of particle detection, "The detector clicks only if the particle goes through the right-hand slit, where the detector is located. But when the detector fails to click, meaning the particle has gone through the left-hand slit, the interference pattern is still destroyed—that is, the measurement (of nothing) still disturbs the particle's wave. The particle need not ever come close to the detector. (Are you dizzy yet?)."[28]

Even the chain of cause and effect seems to be turned around in the two slit detector setup. With a detector behind one slit, photons are detected after their passage through the slits, yet the photons are retroactively constrained to pass through one slit or the other, but never both. The choice to measure a path is "delayed" until after the photons should have already "committed" to pass through both slits, rather than just one.

John Wheeler added a stunning twist with a minor adjustment to the "delayed choice" experiment setup. He showed that the measurement choice could be delayed until after the photon had passed the screen. Therefore, "the precise nature of reality, Wheeler claims, has to await the participation of a conscious observer."[29] You can see why Niels Bohr once said, "If quantum mechanics hasn't profoundly shocked you, you haven't understood it."[30]

This quantum enigma imposes the act of observation as one of the boundary conditions of any experiment on tiny particles. More than this, the delayed choice experiment shows that observation is time invariant; it does not matter when you look, the outcome is still altered by observation. The results of the two slit experiment strongly imply that observation by a consciousness is one of the underlying, and fundamental features of reality, and that observation transcends time.

There could scarcely be a more astonishing development in science than the discovery of conscious observation, and a view to something other than material that is interwoven with matter and energy. The non-material state of potentia and the power of observation demand a non-material cause, and that cause is the Spirit Creator of the Bible. Something of God's own conscious nature has been imprinted onto the smallest units of matter and energy, that are hidden away from normal view. Only in our age have they been discovered.

Strict materialists have no explanation why nature should rest upon a state of possibility, or why a conscious observer should be part and parcel of the fabric of reality. To me the evidence clearly implies a Divine author of consciousness, and that God tailored physics, and the universe, so that conscious beings could arise.

THE SUPER OBSERVER

The prophet Isaiah verifies that God makes measurements, "Who (God) has measured the waters in the hollow of His hand, measured heaven with a span and calculated the dust of the earth in a measure?"[31] The centrality of the observer in quantum measurement also implies the observational nature of God—El Roi, the God Who Sees me.[32] He is the One who makes observations and knows all things.

The creation of the universe is no less dependent on the Super Observer than a quantum mechanics measurement is dependent on a conscious observer. If consciousness really is a fundamental feature of nature, and if no "measurement state change" is made without consciousness, there is no justification to see a stand-alone material universe without a Super Observer. The two are intrinsically bound together, as far as quantum physics is concerned.

The Super Observer is not a superfluous extra step, as atheists say about "adding" God to the physical universe. But without the Super Observer there would not have been a universe to observe. The Super Observer and the quantum events of creation go hand in hand. Therefore, the "why not save a step" argument used to discount the Creator has turned out to be a non sequitur.[33] Instead we have the surpassing beauty of creation.

MEASURING FOR GOD

For Christians, quantum measurement has yet another spiritual counterpart. Scripture attests that in matters of faith, as in quantum particle-wave measurements, you get what you measure for. As Jesus said, "For with the measure you use it will be measured back to you,"[34] and again, "According to your faith be it done to you."[35] To a large extent, we really do create our own spiritual outcome. Deciding to believe in God, or not, is something like the result of a measurement for a wave, or particle in quantum physics.

Likewise, a person can measure for a loving God, or a vindictive God. Eric Metaxas observes, "Either you deem God to be a grace-shedding God, or you condemn Him as a hard taskmaster. ... Jesus seems to be saying, "If you treat me and my Father as though we are 'hard masters,' we will actually be hard masters. The choice is yours (from the parable of the talents, Matthew 25:24)."[36]

For the nonbeliever, God does not exist, and life is a series of accidents that led to human beings. He has measured for "no God" and that is what he has found. Francis Schaeffer wrote of such a person, "The freedom (atheists) sought was an absolute freedom with no limitations. There is no god, nor even a universal law, to limit him, so the individual seeks to express himself with total freedom, and yet, at the same time, he feels the damnation of being in the machine (a soulless material universe). This is the tension of modern man."[37] There can be no deep meaning to life for someone with no sense of God's existence. Therefore, ask God to give you faith.

Believers measure for God's existence by God's power, and they find Him to be good and true. This is not based in reason and evidence alone, but by the revelation of the Holy Spirit, and by observing what God has done. As Jesus told Peter, "flesh and blood has not revealed this to you, but my Father who is in heaven."[38]

The one who earnestly seeks God will find Him. When you find God, you will realize that He was looking for you all along.

CHAPTER ELEVEN

EINSTEIN'S "SPOOKY" ACTION AT A DISTANCE: "THE GOD EFFECT"

"Abide in Me, and I in you. As the branch cannot bear fruit by itself, unless it abides in the vine, neither can you, unless you abide in Me. I am the vine; you are the branches. Whoever abides in Me and I in him, he it is that bears much fruit, for apart from Me you can do nothing."
~ John 15:4, 5 (ESV)

Entanglement normally has a negative connotation, as in being ensnared. But in quantum physics, entanglement is a sort of relational connection between particles. In fact, entanglement has been called the defining property of quantum mechanics. Entangled light particles mysteriously share information over any distance, instantaneously and without communication.

The measurable properties of any photons or particles that have become entangled are shared, and the particles behave as if they were a matched set. They always exhibit the same properties, like a pair of dice that always come up with matching faces. Therefore, entangled objects are said to be in a correlated state.

Formally, entanglement is referred to as a "non-local" phenomenon. Non-locality describes a transcendent sharing of information that would otherwise require direct contact, or the sending of an information signal. Essentially, entanglement violates basic classical assumptions about the way momentum and information is traded among particles, through direct contact. It is as though entangled particles have a built-in instant messaging system, except that no signals or forces are actually sent between the particles. Yet entangled particles react to changes in even one of their number instantly.

Deterministically minded scientists like Albert Einstein were very disturbed by the implications of entanglement.

Einstein termed it a "spooky action at a distance", in a derisive sort of way. He could not believe that such a non-physical connection between physical objects could be real. But quantum mechanics has won the argument through a series of increasingly precise experimental measurements.

Entanglement is so unusual, so wonderful, that Brian Clegg has dubbed it the "God Effect" in his book of the same name. Clegg writes, "The God Effect has an unsettling omnipresence. ... This unbounded linkage permits the remarkable applications of quantum entanglement that are being developed. It enables the distribution of a secret key for data encryption that is impossible to intercept. It plays a fundamental role in the operation of a quantum computer ... and entanglement makes it possible to transfer a particle, and potentially an object, from one place to another without passing through the space in between."[1] More than any other feature of the new physics, entanglement reveals something of the great Mind behind the universe.

ENTANGLEMENT—A MYSTERIOUS LINKAGE

Entangled particles are usually created at the same moment, often by sending a beam of light through a beam splitter. It can also come about when two tiny particles collide. Now imagine that two electrons become entangled in a super conductor with zero net spin, and then are sent off in opposite directions. Next, a measurement of spin is made on one of the electrons and by chance we find it has an "up" spin. After the measurement is performed on the first electron, the spin of the second electron will always measure as a "down" spin.

This happens no matter how quickly the second measurement is made, or how far apart the two electrons are. Moreover, the state of neither electron is decided, until the first measurement is made on one of them. This experiment has been performed with nearly instantaneous first and second measurements, so that no intra particle signals are possible, and it has always checked out. Incidentally, if no spin measurement was made, neither electron would have actually had a spin, but only the possibility of a spin.

As unlikely as it sounds, entanglement has now been established as a central feature of nature. Since 1982, science teams under Alain Aspect, then Anton Zeilinger, and later David Wineland, have performed precise experiments to verify the existence of this "spooky action at a distance". Every deterministic loophole that might allow signals to travel between entangled particles has been closed, and it is very unlikely that future experiments will overturn entanglement.[2] By now, scientists have even entangled two separate diamond crystals at room temperature, using laser light pulses, each comprising more than a million trillion atoms.[3]

A principal consequence of entanglement is that one byte of information is created out of nothing, when particles become entangled. This single byte of information is what is shared by the two particles, however distant.[4] The most mind bending part is that the information is shared only in a form of possibility—the final state of neither particle is determined until a measurement is made on one. The information created by entanglement would seem to quantify the protomentality that Penrose says is associated with every quantum event. This is why the universe seems to be tailor made by God to support conscious beings like us.

Entanglement is a remarkable phenomenon, then, transcending time and space. Ironically, this is something that atheists argue that God can't possibly do—transcend space and time and still act in the universe. Yet such transcendence is displayed in the smallest objects of the physical world, the very building blocks of nature, ubiquitously and continuously throughout the universe. Surely, this is one of the deepest imprints of the Divine, in nature.

GOD AND ENTANGLEMENT

The Bible says that God is everywhere—this is His Omnipresence. He can also be described as the Initial Singularity, the intersection of God and the universe, that causes the universe to come into existence. Frank Tipler describes Christ as the All Presence Singularity, the one who connects the beginning with the end, meaning that everything in the universe is infinitely close to Christ at all times.[5] I take this to be equivalent to saying everything in the universe is entangled with Christ, in the manner of information sharing across any distance. Entanglement is certainly an exact analogy of God's omnipresence.

It seems reasonable to expect that everything that came out of the Initial Singularity should be entangled with that singularity at some level, that is, with the Creator. Such an entanglement is a sufficient means for God to know what is going on in His universe. In this way God could know the state of every particle in the universe at all times.

Jesus posed it this way; "even the hairs of your head are all numbered," which is a more tangible form of saying that God knows our every quantum state.[6] That is, He knows the energy state, or position of every atom in our bodies. I do not know how a non-physical Super Being is entangled with the physical world, but it follows that God should necessarily know the information representing entangled states.

As far as the universe is concerned, this is a passive entanglement, as described in Matthew 5:45, "He makes His sun rise on the evil and on the good, and sends rain on the just and on the unjust."[7] Everyone is blessed by God's common grace in this life, which might be thought of as coming through this passive entanglement. By this means, God can love every conceivable kind of creature, even the unlovable.

Passive entanglement with God means you and I are transparent to Him. He knows everything about you and me, our thoughts and feelings, our actions past, present and future; there is nothing hidden from Him. So there is no point in trying to hide from Him.

Do you recall that observation disrupts light interference, the light and dark patterns on the screen in the two-slit light experiment? An atheist might say that God does not observe the two-slit experiment, and by extension, that He does not observe anything else. Otherwise His observation would cause light to always go through one slit, or the other, and there would never be an interference pattern of light and dark on the screen.

We have the power to see the interference pattern without disrupting it because we are actually seeing light scattered from the experiment—our eye is not in the path of the slits. On the other hand, God is everywhere and, if He were physical, He would disrupt the interference pattern. However, God is non-physical, and He is outside time and space. Assuming His omnipresence is equivalent to entanglement, He can know entangled states without disrupting entanglement, or the light interference pattern on the screen.

Knowing God through His creation only goes so far. We human beings do not really know God in our natural state, but we are separated from Him from birth, having no direct knowledge of His thoughts. I believe we are separated from God in our natural state, both quantitatively and qualitatively, and that it is not really possible to conceive His thoughts. Since He is outside space and time, He is inherently inaccessible to human beings, even sinless ones if any were to exist. For example, before the fall Adam and Eve were only aware of God when He manifested a presence in the Garden of Eden. As Isaiah says, "For as the heavens are higher than the earth, so are My ways higher than your ways, And My thoughts than your thoughts."[8]

We are separated from God on moral grounds too, as St. Paul writes, "All have turned aside; together they have become worthless; no one does good, not even one."[9] Good people and bad people alike are naturally separated from God, even though He knows everything about us. For this reason, God is called Holy, or separate.

Entanglement also illustrates, by analogy, how Jesus Christ could be in direct contact with the full power of the Godhead, even while He inhabited a human body on Earth. The Living Word of God took on the form of Jesus' earthly body, and this is how He could live in human form without sin—by the Spirit of God.[10] Orthodox Christian doctrine, as found in the Nicene Creed of the 4th century, says that the Son, who is the same as God, is begotten by the Father and that the Holy Spirit proceeds from the Father. The gospel writer John also calls the Son the Word, who was with God from the beginning.

Whenever God acts, the Word is there also, and wherever the Word perceives the Father, or the Father perceives the Word, there is the Holy Spirit.[11] All three are of the same substance and are one God, but God's nature is such that His Word and His interaction with the Word are living persons of the Godhead.[12] They are in continual relationship, yet they are one

God.[13] This is why, in the Gospel of John, Jesus had the authority to say, "You search the Scriptures, for in them you think you have eternal life; and these are they which testify of Me."[14]

I believe this Divine interrelationship is deeper than physical entanglement in the world, but God put a type of His own Divine intercourse into the physical universe. The universe, and everything in it then, is relational. This reflects the love that God the Father, Son and Holy Spirit have for one another. This is the archetype of quantum entanglement and the communal behavior of atoms. Though God is far above human beings, He is also very near, seeking a relationship with anyone who is willing.

ENTANGLED IN SALVATION

Of all the world religions, Jesus is the only religious founder that promises to come and live within the believer, in a process that looks just like quantum entanglement. In contrast with every other world religion, Christianity is not based on trying to earn God's favor through good works. Jesus said "unless you eat the flesh of the Son of Man and drink His blood, you have no life in you. Whoever eats My flesh and drinks My blood has eternal life."[15] Essentially, Jesus was speaking of becoming willfully entangled with God by taking something of Christ's essential nature into our being. Eternal life, then, comes by what Jesus Christ has already done for us.

How does this take place in practical terms? What are we to do to please God? People asked Jesus this very thing, as recorded by John, "'What must we do, to be doing the works of God?' Jesus answered them, 'This is the work of God, that you believe in Him whom He has sent.'"[16] This is the willful entanglement with God that gives eternal life, trusting in Jesus Christ. Everything else, that is merely passively entangled with God, will eventually pass away.

Moreover, Jesus told his followers "If you love Me, you will keep My commandments. And I will ask the Father, and He will give you another Helper, to be with you forever."[17] How can one be willfully entangled with God, and know Him unless he loves Him and does what He says? Jesus said, "Whoever abides in Me and I in him, he it is that bears much fruit, for apart from Me you can do nothing."[18] A believer abiding in Christ is very like the process of quantum entanglement, that connects two particles in a transcendent manner. I think prayer is also such a process, by which our thoughts and minds become willfully entangled with God's thoughts, in a communion.

There are many other examples of willful God-believer entanglement in the Bible. Peter wrote a beautiful passage that says believers actually partake of the Divine nature, "He has granted to us His precious and very great promises, so that through them you may become partakers of the Divine nature, having escaped from the corruption that is in the world because of sinful desire."[19] It says in Corinthians, "he who is joined to the Lord becomes one spirit with Him,"[20] and in Ephesians it says, "He may grant you to be strengthened with power through His Spirit in your inner being."[21]

I began to partake of the Divine nature when, as a youngster, I came to believe that God is real, and that Jesus really does care about me. Ever since, I have known in my inner most being that God exists. This does not mean that I have not had disappointments and doubts. I have had doubts and trials, yet I have always had an awareness of God's presence and His goodness. You too can have an intimate relationship with God, if you believe and abide in Jesus Christ.

In Romans it says, "There is therefore now no condemnation to those who are in Christ Jesus, who do not walk according to the flesh, but according to the Spirit."[22] The phrase, "in Christ Jesus," resembles an entanglement of the believer with Christ. First John says, "the blood of Jesus Christ His Son cleanses us from all sin."[23] In the quantum model, we are made clean in God's sight by direct contact with Christ, by the Holy Spirit, by the process of entanglement.

Move forward 2000 years and quantum physicist Heisenberg speaks of this kind of entangled connection with God, "Can you, or anyone else, reach the central order of things or events, whose existence seems beyond doubt, as directly as you can reach the soul of another human being? I am using the term 'soul' quite deliberately so as not to be misunderstood. If you put your question like that, I would say yes."[24]

WHY DON'T WE SEE ENTANGLEMENT?

You may wonder if this is really true. If entanglement is so powerful, why doesn't it percolate into our daily events? Why don't we notice it? Roger Penrose asks a slightly different question, "Why is every particle in the universe not hopelessly entangled? In other words, 'Why do we not just experience an entangled mess, with no resemblance whatsoever to the (almost) classical world that we actually perceive?' ... It is measurements that slash through these entanglements. ... nature herself is continually enacting R-process effects (measurement)."[25] Particles bump into each other and, in effect, measure each other's properties.

You may recall this intra-particle measurement process is called quantum decoherence, and it involves the Penrose protomentality associated with quantum interactions. The result of this natural measurement process, at the atomic level, is our experience with solid everyday objects, rather than with fuzzy atoms.

QUANTUM DECOHERENCE IN FRANCE

In December 2007, after the DAWN and CloudSat spacecraft were launched, I made a three week long trip to southern France to support the Planck spacecraft acoustic and vibration test campaign. I was not really keen on traveling to France for work just before Christmas. My father had just passed away a few months before, succumbing to cancer, and I was still in mourning. I was emotionally flat. I was, however, glad to take my eager wife along. Actually I don't think she would have let me go to southern France without her.

Planck was a super cooled observatory that was designed to make extremely precise observations of the Cosmic Background Radiation. JPL supplied instruments, and a cooler subsystem that chilled the spacecraft detectors to a mere 0.1°K above absolute zero temperature. This made its detectors the coldest known objects in space, until its coolant supply was exhausted. The spacecraft vibration testing was performed at Thales Alenia in Cannes. For the first time, I had a lap top computer that gave me the flexibility to do any part of my job overseas.

I was working with a JPL cryogenic technology engineer, Dave Pearson, to make sure the spacecraft vibration, at JPL supplied equipment, did not exceed its test proven capability.

The natural measurement process of quantum decoherence lends our daily experience comfortable and predictable qualities, even in unfamiliar surroundings. So after a few days, my jet lag and wariness, at being in a country in which I could not speak the language, gave way. I began to delight in exploring the gorgeous south of France, and my depression began to lift.

The French and ESA personnel working Planck had numerous test planning meetings to attend, which were, to my surprise, conducted in English. The European team members hailed from England, Germany, the Netherlands, France and other countries. I remember that one of the French engineers had an uncanny resemblance to Napoleon. Before each meeting I would take a digital copy of the vibration data from the latest test run, and compare it to our assembly requirements and assembly test data. Then I would report my findings during the team meeting, where a consensus was achieved to move forward.

This process went on for three weeks until the test campaign concluded without anomaly. Myra and I were free to return home just three days before Christmas! When we arrived home we were surprised to find that our daughters had put up our Christmas tree, and decorated it beautifully. It was a touching gift for weary travelers.

Years later, I traveled to France again to support the InSight SEIS instrument vibration testing in Toulouse, not once but on three occasions. SEIS is a small but tremendously complex seismic instrument, that was designed to measure Mars quakes and tremors. Several technical challenges had to be overcome in the instrument's development, requiring the joint efforts of CNES and JPL. Problems caused the mission to miss its original launch date. After its final vibration and thermal vacuum tests, the instrument was integrated with the InSight Mars Lander, which landed on Mars in 2018. There it successfully recorded Martian seismic activity for over 4 years.

JPL has afforded me experiences that very few have had, like working in France, visiting high tech companies around the world, and testing "one of a kind" space hardware with some of the highest caliber engineers. No amount of money can buy such experiences. I can definitely say God has been very good to me.

A pessimist might say that the space program is a colossal waste of money and lives, with all the problems we have on Earth. However, it is not as if simply throwing money at our problems would accomplish anything. What humanity has gained in knowledge, technology, and inspiration far surpasses what we have lost in blood and treasure. But treasure has not really been lost. The money wasn't burned in a furnace, but we spent it in our own country, in our own companies, on our own people who built their lives and families with the money they'd earned. Every space dollar spent is worth about 8 dollars to the economy at large. A great deal of wealth has actually been created through space and defense technology expenditures.

The bonanza from space and aerospace technology goes far beyond the stimulation of the economy. New inventions include the seemingly simple, like corning ware, and the complex, like integrated circuits, and atomic clocks. The high tech revolution of computers, the internet and smart phones, are all powered by space age technology. There have been many advances in medical monitoring and technology too. Space exploration also inspires our young people to higher achievement. It certainly inspired me when I was young.

It is human to explore and to seek understanding. I believe that space exploration is more than a distraction for a few lucky human beings. What we are learning of ourselves, and God's creation is of vital importance to our continued development as a species, and possibly to our long term survival. To what would we be reduced if we abandoned the God given urge to discover and grow? No one knew what would come out of Columbus's voyage to the new world, but its value to the world has been incalculable. There is no way of knowing the intellectual and global monetary wealth that the enterprise of space may eventually create.

COMPUTERS AND QUANTUM COMPUTERS

The facts of entanglement may sound crazy to you and you may wonder, skeptically, if it means anything practical? In fact, some level of entanglement has proven to be fundamental to basic properties of matter like heat capacity and magnetism, with measurable effects even at room temperatures.[26] Entanglement does not have to be perfect to influence the behavior of larger physical objects, but it comes in quantifiable degrees; "some systems have a little entanglement; others have a lot."[27]

Even a small degree of entanglement changes the way a physical system operates. Quantum effects have now been detected in plants, enabling the super efficient conversion of sunlight to plant energy during photosynthesis.[28] A magnetically levitated train operates using a superconductive coil, constituting a large scale highly entangled quantum system. So entanglement does percolate into our classical world after all.

Quantum entanglement is also the key mechanism in super- secure data encryption for computers, an unbreakable code. Encryption is a complex secret code for protecting information stored and sent between computers. It is used, for example, by banks and defense agencies. Entanglement is the central phenomenon in the quantum computer, a computer that operates in a fundamentally different way from ordinary computers, and far more powerfully. Quantum computers are now a reality.

A classical computer is essentially a series of switches, called bits, each of which is either on or off. Each switch that is on represents a 1, and every switch that is off is a 0. Since only two values are possible, these switches make calculations using binary numbers representing standard base 10 numbers with 1's and 0's, arranged in the proper way. But classical computers are limited, and they can never simulate non-locality or quantum entanglement.[29]

The amazing difference is that switches in a quantum computer can be both on and off (1 and 0) at the same time, in a superposition of switch states. Superposition means that two states exist at the same moment—switches that are both on and off – and this can only happen if the switches in the quantum computer are entangled. Superposition is similar to a "fade" transition between two photographs on a computer screen. For a brief moment a faint version of both photos can be seen on the same screen.

Entangling switches for use in a computer is something that has been extraordinarily difficult to achieve, on even modest scales, but the payoff for quantum computing is tremendous.[30] Because of entanglement, a large quantum computer will be vastly more powerful than the fastest classical super computers, for certain problems.

In 2007, the Jet Propulsion Laboratory in Pasadena produced a quantum computing chip of 28 qubits (bytes that can be entangled) for a small quantum computer built by D-Wave, of British Columbia, Canada. Now D-Wave is marketing a quantum computer with 1000 qubits. This new unprecedented type of computer can be used to "address problems that are hard for traditional methods to solve": software verification and validation; financial risk analysis; object recognition in images; biological simulations; drug interactions; and genome studies, to name a few.[31] These tasks are more human-like than an ordinary computer can perform, and the quantum computer does other standard types of calculations exponentially faster than a classical computer.[32]

Quantum computers promise to bring about an even bigger revolution in technology than has conventional computing. In fact, the country that leads in quantum computing will dominate the world. Among other things, quantum computing should eventually make true artificial intelligence possible. This could bring about a quantum leap in productivity, and minimize the tedious nature of working with computers. Quantum computing could change life for the better for billions of people, even in unforeseen ways. However, as Elon Musk says, we should have a 'shut off switch' to keep artificial intelligence from getting out of our control.

THE UNIVERSAL QUANTUM COMPUTER

The principal hurdle to large quantum computers is that perfect entanglement is very difficult to achieve on large scales. Entangling the enormous numbers of atoms in a large computer switch array is problematic, since atoms in the array tend to bump and vibrate each other into quantum decoherence—the everyday kind of behavior.

Yet quantum information scientist Seth Lloyd maintains that the universe actually performs computations on the smallest material scales, causing it to become more complex over time. In other words, the universe is an enormous quantum computer.[33]

Mathematicians have demonstrated conclusively that the probability of a complex universe like ours, arising by chance, is so minuscule as to be impossible.[34] The universal quantum computer model says, complexity exists because the universe computes on a quantum level. Lloyd says, "Every atom, every elementary particle registers information. Every collision between atoms, every dynamic change in the universe, no matter how small, processes that information in a systematic fashion."[35] All the information in the universe, then, is said to be the result of the universe's ongoing quantum computation.

Since all information is encoded in physical objects, information is essentially a physical quantity.[36] Therefore, every small particle in the universe naturally processes information, simply by interacting with its neighboring particles. This process is essentially a quantum computation. Lloyd says that man made quantum computers are an example of nature's continuous quantum computation, that we have redirected to calculate what we would like it to calculate.[37]

But how does the universe's quantum computation avoid the disruption of quantum decoherence, or the natural tendency of atoms to bump together and lose their quantum behavior? It can't completely, but even a degree of quantum entanglement can result in a level of quantum information processing, or computing. We have the example of ordinary plants that use quantum processing for super efficient processing of sunlight.

A universe that makes quantum computations points to a Divine author, a Mind of enormous computing power—the source of all wisdom and creative power. The stupendous power of a quantum computer the size of the universe is beyond imagination for anyone except God, who set it in motion and sustains it.

Yet, it is easy to see some of the complexity that God has generated through it. Complexity is all around us, from the lowly bacteria to galaxy clusters in the heavens. Jesus cites the flower blossom as an example of extravagant complexity; "Consider the lilies of the field, how they grow: they neither toil nor spin, yet I tell you, even Solomon in all his glory was not arrayed like one of these.[38]

The unfolding quantum computation of the universe is the object of God's continual observation. Is it possible to see these things without being deeply moved?

CHAPTER TWELVE

ENTANGLEMENT & CONSCIOUSNESS

"Then God said, 'Let us make man in our image, after our likeness. ...
So God created man in His own image, in the image of God
He created him; male and female He created them.'"
~ Genesis 1:26, 27 (ESV)

If the Earth is the natural wonder of the galaxy, then consciousness is the wonder of the universe. Human beings have struggled for centuries to understand the enigmatic nature of consciousness, and the reality of human experience. It is staggering, to paraphrase Einstein, that there are conscious beings like us able to comprehend the universe, and with the ability to manipulate the environment to our benefit. But these are just the kind of attributes one would expect a loving, conscious, and personal God to give to His created beings—to make them conscious and free, able to understand and create.

It is consciousness that separates human beings from mere computing machines, based on electrical switches that are open or closed. In fact, consciousness is one of the most important ways in which we bear the image of God. But what is consciousness exactly?

Many things can be said about consciousness, but a complete definition remains elusive. Consciousness is not the same thing as the mind, just as the mind is not the same thing as the brain. Evan Walker identifies consciousness as, "the carrier of conscious thought. It is what is left when thought is removed, when the mind is stilled ... consciousness is real and nonphysical."[1]

Scientist Amit Goswami's sublime description of it is, "Consciousness is the ground of all being."[2] Pure consciousness is flawless.

Consciousness could be described experientially as the awareness of one's environment, and other conscious beings, while simultaneously observing one's own awareness and thoughts. When you lay awake at night, unable to sleep, watching thoughts run through your own consciousness can be downright hypnotic.

The science of the quantum mind is not yet widely recognized, but it follows the lead of Heisenberg, Herbert, Wolf, Penrose, Walker, and many others. The quantum mind is doubted by some of the same authorities that, only a few years ago, did not believe quantum computers were really performing quantum calculations. Now quantum computers are setting new bench marks in computing, and they are still in their infancy. If you can accept it, the quantum mind theory leads us to the beauty of the mind, and to its Divine author.

CONSCIOUSNESS AND QUANTUM COMPUTING

The materialists' explanation for consciousness seems to boil down to the idea that enough computer power, with the right software, leads to "consciousness". It is also claimed that consciousness is an illusion— that no one is really conscious, and that no one has free will.[3] This is more a case of trying to explain consciousness away, rather than comprehending it. Having experienced consciousness first hand, I do not find this to be a convincing supposition.

Scientists have been pursuing artificial intelligence for several decades, and they still only have rule-based computer programs. These can perform a limited range of things far better than humans, such as storing data, or performing rule based activities like playing chess, or guiding a missile. But no one seriously believes that classical computing machines are conscious. I am, however, willing to concede that computing machines might be regarded as engaging in a very rudimentary form of thinking.

Even quantum computers are not conscious, but sentient quantum computers have existed for a long time— you have one in your head. There is no other explanation for the tremendous computing power of a mere three pounds of human brain. Only a quantum computer of this modest size could handle all the visual data, auditory, and other sensory information, process our thoughts, unconscious actions, and generate a continuous self awareness, all in real time. The case for this theory is impressive, even if it is necessarily circumstantial. There are many reasons to believe that human beings experience consciousness, and are not mere biological machines.

Von Neumann demonstrated that conscious observers participate in creating reality, during the measurement process.[4] Actually, this backs the common sense view most people have always had, that deliberate and willful human thought changes what happens in the world. Furthermore, thoughts have an insubstantial substance, just like Heisenberg's potentia state of unmeasured particles. In other words, our thoughts are like possibilities; some thoughts find a physical manifestation, causing a change in the physical world, and others do not. It turns out that quantum strangeness is not always so strange.

Moreover, conscious observers are not simply computers. Goswami points out that, "Richard Feynman once proved mathematically that a classical computer can never simulate nonlocality."[5] That is to say, even the most powerful classical computers cannot simulate quantum effects. But you have imagined them as you read this book. Remember picturing a computer switch that is both on and off at the same time? Nor can ordinary computers engage in the more abstract forms of mathematical thinking, or derive equations like human beings.

Malcolm Longair says, "It often comes as a surprise that the most rigorously logical of the sciences, abstract mathematics, cannot be programmed on a digital computer, no matter how accurate it is and how large its memory. Such a computer cannot discover mathematical theorems in the way that human mathematicians do. This surprising conclusion is derived from a variant of what is called Godel's Theorem. Roger (Penrose) interprets this to mean that the processes of mathematical thinking, and by extension all thinking and conscious behaviour, are carried out by 'non computational' means."[6]

Non-computational thinking means humans can 'see' in a sudden realization the solution to a math problem, or the solution to a design problem, without making calculations.

Penrose concludes, "Human beings develop this quality of general understanding and it is not a computational quality because mathematical understanding is not." Penrose cites a prime example of this, "The Platonic notion of a natural number (1, 2, 3, 4, 5, etc.) can be abstracted by a child, from just a few simple examples."[7] A classic computer is entirely incapable of such an abstraction. Seth Lloyd recounts that, "the British mathematician Alan Turing showed that self-reference leads to uncomputability in computers."[8] In other words, it is fundamentally impossible for your desktop computer to contemplate itself.

Rodger Penrose, and others have proposed that tiny synaptic structures may provide the necessary physical isolation for quantum activity to be manifest in a prevalent way in the human brain. In particular, Penrose speculates that fine microtubules at the brain's synapses might be the site of quantum coherence.[9] Quantum coherence is another term for the entanglement of electrons in the brain. If true, the human brain is optimized at the smallest scales for conscious experience.

Quantum mind theory says that consciousness arises in human beings in conjunction with the interactions of entangled electrons that transfer, or tunnel, from synapse to synapse within the brain. As electrons tunnel across the brain, they form electron waves that interconnect the various parts of the brain, so that information is shared across its span.[10] More importantly, entangled electrons in the brain exist in a quantum state of potential, being in two states at once, leading to super-powered quantum computing.

Biological test data by Katz and Milhei support the postulate of quantum entangled activity at the brain synapses. The actual firing characteristics of the synapses, in the human brain, match the quantum theory for the phenomenon, hand in glove.[11] It is telling that many biological optical systems can detect the arrival of a single photon at the eye's retina, in a totally dark room. Schroeder writes, "a single quantum of light, the photon, striking the eye's retina can cause the retina to initiate a signal to the brain. That means our brain is sensitive to quantum effects."[12]

Some critics argue that the frequencies of the electrical waves associated with consciousness, are too low for a quantum mechanical source. But any number of brain wave frequencies can be created by electron wave addition, as vast numbers of small electron wavelets add to form longer, lower frequency brain waves. In this way, electron waves add into larger waves, in an exact analogy to waves in water. The rapid motion of tiny water molecules add to form wavelets, and these wavelets combine to create larger water waves, in an enormous range of wave sizes.

Other recent experiments have verified that consciousness is global in nature and not isolated to one location, or part of the brain.[13] This supports another Penrose postulate, "... that consciousness is something global. Therefore, any physical process responsible for consciousness would have to be something with an essentially global character. Quantum coherence (entanglement over a distance) certainly fits the bill in this respect."[14]

The manner in which the mind works also points to quantum computing in human beings. People do not experience a single monolithic line of thought, in the manner of a classical computer that crunches a long calculation. Instead, our thoughts are intertwined streams, some thoughts conflicting with others, yet existing within our awareness simultaneously. Layers of tactile sensations, sight and sound, touch, taste and smell, can all blend together in the same beautiful moment. This experience is a form of wave addition, common to quantum mechanical phenomena.

In stark contrast to classical computers, human beings process vast amounts of visual, auditory, and other sensory data continuously, and effortlessly. We can pick out objects from the clutter of visual data bombarding our eyes, or decipher one person's speech from the din of a crowded room.

These things are trivially easy for people with undamaged brains, because of the mind's quantum computing ability to deconstruct complex light and sound waves in real time. People effortlessly interpret vast amounts of visual information, and break it down in the same way the Schrödinger equation reduces complex quantum states to a superposition of individual waves. In this case, waves within a field of consciousness.

All people experience meandering thought patterns, and we frequently have to corral our thoughts back to the task at hand. This unavoidable mental behavior is consistent with the random nature of quantum mechanical events. What's more, new ideas come to mind suddenly, like a quantum state change, giving one a sudden burst of pleasure in the sheer delight of discovery.

Creativity can be enhanced using techniques that play on the quantum mechanical model of the mind. A mind open to new possibilities, and the persistent grappling with a problem, both enhance the chance of a low-probability solution. New experiences can also trigger new ideas on a completely unrelated matter, in a seemingly random way. Taking temporary leave of a problem also takes advantage of unconscious (unobserved) quantum computing, often producing a novel solution. We can direct our mind to do something by simply giving it an instruction, and the quantum processor in our head performs it. Athletes talk of being in the zone, performing at their peak without distraction from ego, or self talk. This too is a manifestation of quantum computing. Finally, brainstorming with other people takes advantage of a non-local sharing of ideas —parallel quantum processing, if you will.[15] These ways of increasing creativity may be fairly obvious, but the point is that all of them fit into the quantum mind model.

Worry fits the mold too. Like the evil twin of creativity, worry and rumination tend to constrict the number of possibilities open to the one doing the worrying, limiting the potential for solutions to the very problems being worried about. Planning and changing what can be changed is good, but the immense volume of information, in which we live and move, shows how futile worry really is. We are only aware of a small fraction of our environment, much less control all that information.

This reinforces what the Lord said about worry, "Therefore I tell you, do not be anxious about your life, ... which of you by being anxious can add a single hour to his span of life?"[16] Some of us, myself included, have to work against our own natures to trust God for the things we cannot control, and take advantage of the power of unconscious quantum computing.

THE QUANTUM MIND

Evan Walker outlines a working quantum model of the human mind that accurately depicts the function and capabilities of the human mind, the will, and even why we need sleep, to reset energy states in the brain.[17]

The quantum mind theory says consciousness takes on a unique form, or personality, for each individual based on the structure of our brains, which varies with genetic makeup, individual experiences, and habitual decision patterns. This imparts a personal identity, while our memories, conscience, and emotions guide us in making moral choices, and in preferences of taste.

It turns out the classic computing activity of the human brain also requires a level of quantum entanglement. Goswami explains that, "for intelligence to operate, the firing of one neuron must be accompanied by the firing of many correlated neurons at macroscopic distances—as much as ten centimeters—which is the width of the cortical tissue. In order for this to happen, notes Wolf, we need nonlocal correlations ... existing at the molecular level in our brain, at our synapses. Thus, even our ordinary thinking depends on the nature of quantum events."[18]

Goswami goes on to counter a common scientific objection to the quantum mind theory, "Biologists often argue that consciousness must be an epiphenomenon of the brain because changing the brain by natural damage or drugs changes conscious events. Yes, says the quantum theorist, because changing the measurement apparatus (the brain) does certainly change what can be measured, and therefore, change the event.[19] This means the quantum mind theory is consistent with phenomena arising from brain damage and drug induced states.

CONSCIENCE AND THE WILL

The human conscience is also consistent with the quantum theory of mind. C.S. Lewis wrote, "If there was a controlling power outside the universe, it could not show itself to us as one of the facts inside the universe— no more than the architect of a house could actually be a wall, or staircase, or fireplace in that house. The only way in which we could expect it to show itself would be inside ourselves as an influence, or a command trying to get us to behave in a certain way. And that is just what we do find inside ourselves."[20] This is like a degree of quantum entanglement of God with a person's inner being. The conscience operates like an inner law, yet we are free to listen to conscience, or not. It can also be reprogrammed for good, or bad. Repeated violations of the inner law can sear one's conscience, rendering it inoperative in part, or in whole.

The human will has a quantum character too. Changing one's mind is like turning one switch on, and another off. We can replace old thoughts by laying hold of a new better idea, simply by telling our quantum mind to do so. Habitual thought patterns do work against our changing, and the settings for the switches in our mind can reset themselves spontaneously in a random fashion. When this occurs, we must keep redirecting our mind to the new better idea, in an act of the will.

Most interestingly, the will gives us influence beyond ourselves. Walker describes the will's "mind-bending" interaction with the world, "this will channel causes the events in the brain and those in the external world to go hand in hand with what happens in our consciousness. We are saying that our mind can affect matter—even other brains—and that distant matter and minds can have an effect on us. What we have here, what is forced on us by the formalism of quantum mechanics itself, is something that sounds like telepathy or psychokinesis; it is exactly what Einstein feared to be the implications of quantum mechanics."[21]

Walker elaborates, "By creating the possibilities that we experience as consciousness and by selecting—by willing—which synapse will fire, mind brings into reality each moment's thoughts, experiences, and actions."[22] The will, then, is the stream of thought that directs the body to act in the world. The initiation and execution of an act of the will is hidden from sight, buried within our mind's quantum computer.

From here Walker reaches a startling conclusion, "Unlike the consciousness, our will is not restricted to the tiny space of the brain cavity. Everything we touch, see, or experience in any way that becomes caught up in that special aspect of the quantum nature of matter, will retain a link back to our mind. ...

The will channel (part of the mind) is a link that transcends space, and because physicists have found that something called Lorentz invariance (no privileged frame of reference) always holds, this (human) will must transcend time as well."[23]

Put simply, we change what happens in the world by willing it to be. Moreover, the will's influence reaches beyond time and space, in a time independent manner similar to observation.

THE EQUIVALENCE OF OBSERVERS

The equivalence of observers (no privileged frame of reference), means that every observer always sees a quantum event occurring with the same result.[24] People do, of course, reach different conclusions about complex issues. We all have different information, different processing capability, and each individual's thought patterns are essentially unique, because the structure of each brain and life experience is unique. More than this, we have different goals and experiences, we make different moral choices, and we desire different outcomes.

People make mistakes of perception simply because we are engulfed by so much more data than we can process. I used to believe that I was such a reliable observer of detail that I did not need to work hard to get things right. This less than thorough approach got me into trouble during my time on Mars Observer, when I missed a contractor's incorrect vibration test input and a cooler failed its test. It was a bitter lesson, but I know now that everyone misperceives things at times, especially in stressful situations when the mind can be distracted.

But if our measuring devices—our five senses and the brain—are not damaged, and if we have the same physical frame of reference, every observer will see the same outcome occur. Even though the vast majority of our conscious experience is isolated to our own bodies, consciousness does have this universal and monolithic quality. One person's awareness is just like another person's awareness.

SHARED KNOWLEDGE

There could be no better description than entanglement for what happens in coordinated and purposeful group activity, or in personal relationships. John Preskill of Cal Tech sees his scientific collaborators in terms of entanglement; "We're an entangled community of scientists with different backgrounds, but with enough common ground to engage with one another fruitfully. It's really exciting."[25]

God once remarked on the power of such entangled collaboration saying, "they are one people, and they have all one language, and this is only the beginning of what they will do. And nothing that they propose to do will now be impossible for them."[26] Surely, our ability to bend reality to our own advantage is one of the deepest impressions of the Divine nature within us.

People of a new-age disposition mistakenly think that this means that they create their own reality, instead of God. But this is a misinterpretation. What actually occurs in life is a small subset of what we really want to occur. Clearly, we live in a vast sea of quantum events that are beyond our control. Yet many people, even those not of a new-age persuasion, incorrectly conclude that they owe all their success to themselves alone, instead of God. He gives us our abilities and resources.

Herbert insists that quantum entanglement leads to an extraordinary view of shared knowledge, "if ordinary awareness is a private manifestation of deep quantum reality, Bell's theorem requires our quantum knowledge to be non-local, instantly linked to everything it has previously touched."[27] Consciousness transcends time and space because it arises from entanglement. So human consciousness is transcendent just as God is transcendent, though on an incomparably smaller scale.

This deep connection of shared knowledge happens naturally with lovers, just as God said, "Therefore a man shall leave his father and mother and hold fast to his wife, and the two shall become one flesh. So they are no longer two but one flesh." [28] Moreover, intercourse between a husband and wife bears another trademark of quantum physics— possibility—for love fulfilled and for human conception.

I have a soul connection with my wife even though I am not aware of it most of the time. I don't feel whole without her and when I travel for work by myself I am keenly aware of a void. Forming a marital bond with her and having children are the most rewarding things that I have ever done. I have experienced a sense of completion that I never thought possible in my younger days. This connection seems to come to the fore only when it is not being watched.

The other day my wife said she needed something at Barnes & Noble, but she didn't say what. I parked the car, we entered the store and she wandered towards the parenting section of the store. I followed without saying a word. We turned into an aisle at the end of a bookshelf, and immediately my eye was drawn to the cover of a book. I pointed at it and read the first part of the title out loud, "The Happiest Toddler" (by Harvey Karp).

To my surprise Myra said, "That is the book I was looking for!" I exclaimed, "We just had a quantum entangled experience!" and she laughed in agreement. Out of the thousands of books in the store, we located the book cooperatively, with virtually no searching, and without my wife verbalizing her purpose. Maybe we just had toddlers on our minds, but it seemed to us more than a coincidence.

A PERSONAL GOD AND THE SOUL

Doctor Walker concludes that physics points to a personal God, "We find that what we had thought was an independent and objective physical world is in fact contingent on the observer, on our combined consciousness, in a most basic way. And it follows that the God we find must be a personal God."[29]

Walker then turns his attention to us, "it has only been with the advent of quantum theory that we have discovered proof that we exist as something more than pieces of matter. In the development of quantum theory, the observer emerges as a co-equal in the foundry of creation."[30] We have a real spirit nature, and there is no actual division between the physical and the spiritual. This view is entirely consistent with the Bible.

People are not hapless victims of nature, but what we think we do, and that which we do changes the world. Choices made in the past can indeed complicate decisions that we might need to make in the present, but it is still possible to change and grow. We can merge our wills with other people's, and together we can modify our natural surroundings, build shelter and our knowledge base. We develop technologies and organize societies that increase our odds of survival. In fact, every purposeful thing that we humans do is a matter of observation and state selection, by a conscious act of will.

ENTANGLEMENT AND LIFE?

It has been seriously suggested by scientists Vlatko Vedral and Johnjoe McFadden that entanglement might even form the basis of life and its underlying processes.[31, 32] Niels Bohr anticipated this connection eighty years ago saying, "the fact that consciousness, as we know it, is inseparably connected with life ought to prepare us for finding that the very problem of the distinction between the living and the dead escapes comprehension in the ordinary sense of the word."[33]

This would mean that the underlying protomentality of tiny quantum interactions also contains the spark of life. There would be no need for any other "ghost in the machine" for life to arise.[34] Should this be a surprise when Jesus told us that, "He is not the God of the dead, but the God of the living?"[35]

THE GOD WHO IS THERE

Is it any wonder that atheists generally deny the quantum model of the mind? The quantum mind points so unambiguously to God's own consciousness that it affronts the materialists' worldview. Atheists would have to admit that something exists beyond mere matter, and that there really is mystery in life that cannot be explained in material terms. Quantum mechanics has revealed that consciousness is one of the principle features of the universe, and not one of its effects.

Most atheists see man as a biological machine with no power to determine his or her own destiny. But rational thought would not be possible for such a biological machine. A reasoned basis of the atheistic worldview would also not be possible. Playing on the view of man as biological machine, postmodernists see all human actions as 'inevitable, rather than thought out.' By rejecting truth they descend into irrationality. Mathematician John Lenox submits a contrasting view, "the biblical worldview, that traces the origin of human rationality to the fact that we are created in the image of a rational God, makes real sense as an explanation of why we can do science."[36]

As human beings, we find ourselves in consciousness and when we see ourselves, we may find God looking at us. He is the spectacular Mind—the first Observer—who brought the proto-conscious substrate of the universe into existence. Ours is a universe designed from the beginning to support conscious beings like us, who bear the image of His Super Consciousness. We have been given the ability to make an observation that God exists, a realization without computation, like a measurement made by the power of the Holy Spirit.

What greater confirmation for God's authorship of personality and mind could there be than this?

CHAPTER THIRTEEN

TELEPORTATION & CHRIST'S MISSION

"For He made Him who knew no sin to be sin for us, that we might become the righteousness of God in Him."
~ 2 Corinthians 5:21, New King James Version

You may think teleportation is just Star Trek science fiction, like an intrepid spaceman beaming down to a planet's surface. In the movie Dune it was called "traveling without moving". But now it has actually been done with photons of light and atoms. Scientists have teleported information from one atom to another, exactly reproducing the original atom by taking advantage of quantum entanglement.[1] This sophisticated new technology is known as quantum teleportation.

Dr. Hanson of the Delft University of Technology in the Netherlands believes that, "in principle it should be possible to teleport ourselves from one place to another."[2] It would however, require a fantastically powerful quantum computer, along with the ability to entangle and manipulate an inconceivable number of atoms.

TELEPORTATION AND THE BIBLE

Maybe one day in the distant future the teleportation of humans will be possible, but God, it seems, has already teleported people. There are a few instances in the Bible that read like a supernatural quantum teleportation.

The Bible says of Enoch, "And Enoch walked with God; and he was not, for God took him."[3] Centuries later, after His resurrection from the dead, Jesus appeared to His disciples while they were behind locked doors, "Jesus came and stood among them and said to them, 'Peace be with you.'"[4]

In Acts, the Lord's apostles were once removed mysteriously from prison, "When the officers came and did not find them in the prison, they returned and reported, saying, 'Indeed we found the prison shut securely, and the guards standing outside before the doors; but when we opened them, we found no one inside!'"[5] The undisturbed lock and guard implies a supernatural teleportation of the apostles.

Later, the apostle Phillip was teleported from Gaza, south of Jerusalem, to Azotus several miles away. The episode is recounted in the book of Acts, "Philip and the eunuch went down into the water, and he baptized him. Now when they came up out of the water, the Spirit of the Lord caught Philip away, so that the eunuch saw him no more; and he went on his way rejoicing. But Philip was found at Azotus."[6] These Biblical accounts are consistent with quantum entanglement and teleportation.

HOW TELEPORTATION WORKS

The uncertainty principle prohibits obtaining complete information about any object that might be used to exactly reproduce it down to its quantum states. So you might say, "teleportation must be a fraud!" But teleportation gets around the Heisenberg limitation on knowledge by taking advantage of a three-way entanglement.

An object can be teleported to a distant receiving station only if every atom involved in the process can be perfectly entangled with no errors, and where the resulting entangled quantum states are not actually measured. Astonishingly, teleportation works because no one gets to see what goes on behind the scenes; the uncertainty principle is never violated.

Anton Zeilinger, who performed the first teleportation using light, outlines how the teleportation of light works.[7] I will summarize that story here using the foil of teleporting a person.

Imagine that Bill has volunteered to be the first person teleported from the Earth's Quantum Sending Station, to a Moon Base receiving station. Bill bravely steps into the Earth transporter measurement chamber. An adjacent chamber contains an equal mass of organic material, and there is a second mass of material like it at the Moon Base. The atoms of these two separate organic masses have already been entangled through a special process—they share information in the spooky quantum way.

Next, a process called a Bell state measurement is performed on Bill, and the adjacent earth bound organic material. This operation measures joint properties of Bill's atoms and those of the adjacent organic material, without finding the properties of the individual atoms. It also produces a vast amount of random data that is crucial to the teleportation. In the process, the atoms comprising Bill, the organic material on the Earth, and the organic material on the Moon become interlinked in a three way entanglement.

All the information that was Bill is now shared with the organic material on the Moon, altering the quantum states of the atoms there. Unfortunately, Bill on Earth has been destroyed in the entanglement process.[8] He is now just a mass of entangled atoms in a jumbled random quantum state. Gulp!!

Next, Earth Base sends an ordinary radio message to the Moon station describing the random data resulting from the Bell state measurement performed on Earth. The necessity of this classical information limits teleportation to the speed of light.

The Moon Base scientists use the ordinary radio data to process the entangled organic material on the Moon, recreating Bill down to the exact quantum state of every atom.[9] When the process is finished the atoms are no longer entangled, and Bill is very much alive on the Moon, without having traveled there. But earth Bill is gone—a classical object like a person can't be in two places at once!

If you find teleportation more than a bit confusing don't worry. It confuses me, especially the processing of Bill's every atom. Anton Zeilinger says he does not understand it either.

But, is there a practical side of teleportation? As you might have guessed, there is. Computer switches register information and perform calculations. Teleportation can be used to transfer exact switch states, or slightly modified switch states, between quantum processors. In other words, teleportation can move information from one switch to another within a quantum computer, a requisite for performing computations in a quantum computer. Such entangled switch transfers are impossible in standard digital computers.

THE DIVINE QUANTUM ANALOGY

It is a point of the Christian faith that the essence of our being lives on with God, after it leaves the physical body in death. Christ's mission on Earth was to teach us about God and to make it possible for us to be with Him in Heaven. This means the quantum states (information) that comprise the soul must be stable after the body is dead, possibly constrained by forces in unseen dimensions. In any event, entering Heaven requires that God sustain the human soul as it passes from this world into the next.

It may be that Heaven exists in another universe next to our own. No one knows where heaven is, but it is not in this universe. This universe and everything in it has an end, unlike Heaven, which is a place of eternal life in the presence of God. I don't think people enter heaven through teleportation, except perhaps for Enoch. Maybe getting there is a kind of inter-dimensional travel outside our universe. But, one thing is sure, to get there you need to have a relationship with God. You need to be entangled with Jesus Christ.

As unbelievable as it may sound, the principal tenets of Christianity, the acts of God that bring about eternal life, can be posed in quantum mechanical terms. In particular, entanglement and teleportation lead to a series of stunning Christian spiritual analogies.

To rephrase the gospel narrative, eternal life begins with the entanglement of one's mind and will with Christ, in an act of faith. The intimate connectivity of entangled particles, that share information over any distance, shows how Christ can live in us, just as He promised. It is not the entirety of one's mind, or will that is entangled with God. Being in Christ is like a person who's spiritual state is partly correlated with Christ's nature. We receive a measure of His nature within ourselves by quantum entanglement, or something very like it, by the Holy Spirit.

Since our minds arise from entangled interactions within our bodies, quantum entanglement is a sufficient means for God to share the information in our minds. This is a new way of describing the indwelling of the Holy Spirit, as an entangled sharing of information between Christ and believers. Our degree of entanglement with Christ is determined, in part, by how closely we abide in Him.

God's saving act is described in the Bible as an act of substitution—Christ's death in place of our own. Saint Paul expressed this as the transfer of our sins to Christ, and His righteousness to all believers, "He (God) made Him (Christ) who knew no sin to be sin for us, that we might become the righteousness of God in Him."[10] Christ becoming sin for us suggests an exchange from believers to Christ, or a sharing of quantum states (or information) related to our sin. We being righteous "in Him" speaks to our being made right by an entanglement with Christ. By becoming willfully entangled with Christ in this life, we gain a measure of His good attributes, while He takes on our worst attributes.

The description of salvation in Revelation 1:5 also fits the entanglement model, "Jesus Christ, ... loved us and washed us from our sins in His own blood."[11] Being washed in the blood of Jesus speaks to an intimate connection (entanglement) with Christ that removes, or neutralizes our sin before God.

It seems to me teleportation aptly describes the process of how our sins were put onto Christ, as He paid the price for our sins on the cross. Teleportation is the only means of transferring exact quantum states (information) from one quantum computer to another, or in this case, from one human soul to Christ.

The need for complete entanglement for teleportation to work, and the attending destruction of the object being teleported, strongly suggests that Christ could only have taken on our sin states by dying. The teleportation of information from a human soul can only occur when physical death frees the soul from the body. The soul can then become more fully entangled with Christ, and a person's quantum states related to sin can finally be transferred to Him in full.

The physicality of this view of Christ's sacrifice harmonizes perfectly with His bodily mission to save flesh and blood people. It also corroborates what Isaiah says, that a price had to be paid to cover our sin, "He was pierced for our transgressions; He was crushed for our iniquities; upon Him was the chastisement that brought us peace, and with His wounds we are healed."[12]

In this quantum model, God's saving teleportation involves a three-way entanglement, as in the teleportation of information.

However, in this case it is the entanglement of certain states of the believer's soul, Christ and the Holy Spirit.

Christ came to make God understandable to us, and to directly experience the human dilemma, and natural death. Hebrews 4:15 says, "we have a savior who is not unsympathetic, having suffered as one of us."[13] Most of all He came to save us from our sins, and end our separation from God. Before His crucifixion, Jesus said to God the Father, "O My Father, if it is possible, let this cup pass from Me; nevertheless, not as I will, but as You will."[14] He died within a few agonizing hours on the cross.

Why such a terrible death? Jesus immersed Himself in the worst impulses of mankind in His crucifixion, to confront and take on our sins. In His death, He experienced the worst of human nature first hand. He called this process a baptism, but it can also be seen as an entanglement with evil, in order to overcome it, in His resurrection. God gave up His Son, not because of barbarism, as some atheists charge, but because there was no other way to save you and me. The shame and brutality of the cross was not incidental, but we are to see our own shamefulness and brutality there.

It seems that Christ had to come in human form in order to teleport sin from us to Himself, that is, to teleport quantum states between two similar quantum computers. Hebrews 2:17 seems to say this very thing, "Therefore he had to be made *like his brothers in every respect*, so that he might become a merciful and faithful high priest in the service of God, to make propitiation (payment or reparation) for the sins of the people."[15]

The quantum analogy also implies a deep purpose in our present suffering and death. Those who believe in Christ are saved now, but we don't yet possess the prize in full. Most of our quantum states are still in classical states, interacting intimately with the physical world. The resettling of our complete spiritual states into Heaven, minus our sin nature, cannot occur until we die, and God makes our souls more perfectly coherent with Christ. This does not mean we justify ourselves by dying; only that the transfer of our sin to Christ on the cross is finally completed when we die.

The transfer of spiritual states at death may sound backwards to you, but God's saving act takes place in a time-independent way that mirrors the time independence of quantum observation. God Himself, the One doing the work, is outside time. He says of Himself, "I am God, and there is none like Me, declaring the end from the beginning, and from ancient times things that are not yet done."[16]

Tipler describes Christ as the All Presence Singularity, who is infinitely close to everything in the universe at all times.[17] Because Christ is in direct contact with everything, no matter when a person dies, their spirit can become entangled with Him, and their sins can be transfer to Him in full.

This is another way of saying that anyone who looks on Christ and believes— whoever willfully entangles himself with the Savior—is transformed no matter when they live. Christ's name in Revelation 13:8 is, "The Lamb slain from the foundation of the world."[18] This name speaks of the time independence of Christ's sacrifice and the process of salvation. This passage clearly indicates that the central event of Christianity was conceived and established from the foundation of the universe, when God created quantum mechanics. Furthermore, Christ is not destroyed for humanity ever again, but only once: "Christ was offered once to bear the sins of many."[19]

God's Spirit in us means life for us now, even though as human beings we still suffer and die in this world. Saint Paul wrote, "yet at present we do not see all things subjected to Him," but we still struggle against our sin natures.[20] We fully realize the promise of eternal life once we die, as it says in Hebrews, "Now faith is the substance of things hoped for, the evidence of things not seen."[21]

Obviously, dying does not entangle one's body with any earthly thing, and no physical teleportation is taking place when someone dies. Life stops, the body decays, and that is the end of us physically. Jesus declared that the body will one day be resurrected, but He also said that eternal life comes of the Spirit.[22, 23] The teleportation of states involved in eternal life, as I describe it here, are the quantum states of the mind and soul, and not the physical body.

If you accept the proposition that we are essentially information encoded within our bodies, that our soul lives on after death, and if you believe that Christ took on your sins in

His death, then it is reasonable to accept the teleportation of exact quantum states in salvation by God.

CHRIST IS THE WAY

Jesus said, "I am the way, and the truth, and the life. No one comes to the Father except through Me," declaring Himself not just to be truthful, but to be the truth incarnate, and the only real path to God the Father.[24] This seems arbitrary and noninclusive to many people, and they can't believe that God would require such a narrow path to eternal life. But consider who Christ is—God's living Word, the very expression of God the Father.[25] It is not really possible to know God, or come to Him without an exchange of information, that is, the intellectual content of God's Word, which is the person of Jesus Christ.

This does not really mean that those who have not heard about Christ, or have not yet made a deliberate decision for Christ are doomed to hell. We cannot really know the eventual fate of anyone who does not yet believe. Only God knows a person's last thoughts.

Anyone who is brought face to face with God after death necessarily encounters Christ. Paul writes of such post-death encounters with God, "For now we see in a mirror, dimly, but then face to face. Now I know in part, but then I shall know just as I also am known."[26] Besides, God does not really need our help to save anybody. Anecdotal reports from countries closed to the gospel tell of many people who are coming to faith through personal appearances of Jesus Christ, in dreams and visions.

Having said all that, everyone should act on what they know of Christ with a sense of urgency. All of us are invited by Christ to know God personally. Why wait to make peace with God until there is no one to guide you, and no recourse to God's judgment of your soul? Now is the time to "Seek the Lord while He may be found," while you may be sure of His grace.[27]

It is those who have a willful relationship with God, entangling their heart, soul, and mind with Him in an act of surrender, who really know God. This relationship with God, through Jesus Christ, is the core feature of Christianity. A believer's chief aim ought to be deepening this relationship. If you don't have this Divine relationship you are not yet really a Christian. Fortunately for all of us, Jesus says it only takes a small faith, the size of a "mustard seed", to have eternal life.[28]

Super secure transactions between entangled quantum computers are analogous to eternal security in salvation. Such quantum transfers of data are tamper proof. Similarly, Jesus declared that believers are secure in Him, "I give them eternal life, and they shall never perish; neither shall anyone snatch them out of My hand,"[29] Again, Christ said in Revelation 3:5, "The one who is victorious will, like them, be dressed in white. I will never blot out the name of that person from the book of life".[30]

The entanglement of our spirit with Christ and our eternal security is entirely God's doing. It does not depend on us. This is true even though we have free will to choose to follow God.

WHAT SEALS BELIEVERS?

What exactly is it that seals us in eternal life? What is it that changes us? Jesus tells us that it is His life giving word, "It is the Spirit who gives life; the flesh is no help at all. The words that I have spoken to you are spirit and life."[31]

Jesus illustrates this process with a parable of seed cast upon different types of soil. In the story, the seed that falls on good soil takes root and grows. The good soil represents those who are receptive to God's word and honestly accept it. The seed is the good news of the gospel, which takes root in the good soil and it produces grain enough for a harvest.[32]

The entanglement leading to eternal life is not a matter of merely reading the words of Christ. It is the living Word, Christ Jesus, that believers willingly receive in themselves, so that the Word takes root in them. This is why learning and professing (praying) Bible verses can so powerfully change a person's thinking and state of mind. We are not yet fully correlated with Christ, in the quantum mechanical analogy, but that which is necessary to convert the believer is correlated with Christ, by the Holy Spirit. Once we truly surrender ourselves to God, and agree to walk in His way, Christ's sacrifice covers all our sin, past, present and future.

ENTANGLEMENT WITH CHRIST CHANGES US

Saint Paul says that, "if anyone is in Christ, he is a new creation. The old has passed away; behold, the new has come."[33] Once converted, the security of one's salvation is God's doing. It is no longer an issue of human free will, which has been exercised by the true believer in a time independent fashion. John MacArthur once said, "If you could lose your salvation you would." The uncertainty principle backs this view, that if it were possible, it would eventually occur. It is because God seals us in Christ that we have a genuine hope for eternal life.

Eternal life is by the Spirit, but it cannot take place without real state changes in the believer's mind, body, and soul that become manifest in the material world. That is why Christ said, "every tree that does not bear good fruit is cut down and thrown into the fire. Therefore, by their fruits you will know them."[34]

Saint James wrote in the same vein saying, "faith without works is dead."[35] In fact, Jesus tells us that to get into God's paradise we must be born again.[36] If we are willfully entangled with Him, we have access to the power of the new life now. Yet, our testimony is in the goodness of Christ, that very often stands in contrast to our own behavior.

We abide in Him by faith, which comes by His word. Yet, in a very real sense, for a new convert, faith in Christ exists only as a possibility until it is measured and observed. Quantum measurements of our character are unavoidable because every quantum interaction comprises a measurement. My faith may be measured in ways that are different from the measurement of your faith. Whatever the tests, choices that we make reveal the reality of our faith and love, or the lack thereof. Most measurements we experience are incidental, while others can be monumental and life changing. Usually, the tests that we consider personal failures are the ones by which we learn the most. It is by this testing that we grow and abide more willingly in Christ.

In Genesis 22 Abraham was sorely tested when God asked him to offer up his son as a sacrifice. God stopped Abraham in the act of sacrificing his son, and He provided a ram instead.

Then God told Abraham, "now I know that you fear God, since you have not withheld your son, your only son, from Me."[37] God observed the true intent of Abraham's soul by completing this measurement.

Job, in one of the oldest books in the Bible, "was blameless and upright, one who feared God and turned away from evil."[38] Nevertheless, at Satan's prompting Job was tested to the limits of human endurance. He lost his health, his family and virtually everything that he owned. He desperately wanted someone to mediate between him and the Almighty, but Christ our intercessor had not yet been revealed.[39] Even so, Job declared his unswerving trust in God, saying, "Though He slay me, yet will I trust Him."[40] Later, Job prophesied that God would provide a mediator and redeemer who would grant him new life after death, "For I know that my Redeemer lives, and He shall stand at last on the earth (Jesus Christ); and after my skin is destroyed, this I know, that in my flesh I shall see God, Whom I shall see for myself, and my eyes shall behold, and not another."[41] Not long after, Job's trial ended and God restored all that he had lost.

All true believers are also communally entangled in a way through their entanglement with Christ. This union is called the Church. Paul wrote about this saying, "we, being many, are one body in Christ, and individually members of one another,"[42] and Jesus said, "by this all will know that you are My disciples, if you have love for one another."[43] Both verses describe a level of entanglement among all believers, through the Holy Spirit. However, someone can be entangled on a level with members of the Church, you can have friends in the church, without knowing Christ.

As Saint Paul said, the believer must become "a new creation".[44] When we die the information that comprises us must have a new home. The Bible says that in heaven we will have a new kind of body, one that is not subject to the wear of entropy and death, but a body that is completely whole and healthy. Yet we will remain ourselves essentially.

I do not know what our bodies will be like, but Paul wrote that, "the dead will be raised incorruptible, and we shall be changed."[45] Both the living and the dead will be given a new body like Christ's resurrection body.[46] Christ's resurrection is God's guarantee that believers will be new creations in Heaven.

If, as some claim, Christ did not rise from the dead, there can be no eternal life for us.[47] But the resurrection is real.

When Christ was crucified his closest disciples hid in fear for their lives, unable to believe that Jesus would conquer death as He had said. When Christ arose from the dead three days later, His disciples did not believe the first reports that He was no longer dead. But after they saw Him, and touched Him, walked with Him, and ate with Him on multiple occasions, all of them believed.[48] He also appeared to five hundred men and women at a single gathering.[49]

After this, the Holy Spirit gave His disciples a boldness to declare Christ crucified and risen.[50] They were transformed, willing to die for their testimony. One by one, they did all die for their message in far flung places, alone, except for John who was exiled. The disciples died not only for a new faith, but because they attested to the reality of a single seemingly impossible event that they had all observed, that Jesus Christ had risen from the dead, and was alive.

These events were chronicled in great detail, and corroborated by more historical sources than any other event of the ancient world.[51] None of Christ's antagonists have ever been able to explain the empty tomb, which was sealed and kept under Roman guard until His resurrection.[52] Moreover, the scores of Old Testament prophecies that were fulfilled by Christ's life, death and resurrection are unique in all literature.[53]

DOUBTS ARE NATURAL

If you are like me, you may at times feel like you are inadequate to teach others, or worse, not destined for eternal life. This is natural, since none of us are good enough to live in the presence of a perfect God. Maybe you have doubts about God's goodness too.

If you are angry with God over an intractable difficulty, generalized feelings of exasperation and impending doom can be magnified. Perhaps you have unconsciously transferred feelings you had about your parents to God, and you see Him as distant or angry. Maybe you suffer from a compulsion that you have not been able to master. Or maybe you drive three-and-a-half hours to work and back, and there is enough adrenalin coursing through your body to power a ninja warrior. You may wonder if God cares about your plight.

Especially as a young man, I was mortified that I might separate myself from God in a raging temper tantrum. I had a lot of bottled up anger. Nevertheless, salvation is not dependent on feelings, and a temper tantrum cannot terminate our relationship with the heavenly Father. Our qualification for heaven is in knowing Jesus Christ (by entanglement), not in our own merit. Willful entanglement with God is not a feeling, though we may be aware of the connection with God at times.

Indeed, the uncertainty principle would indicate that, since doubts are possible, they are inevitable to a degree. The important thing is how to deal with them. The answer to such doubts and fears is to see oneself realistically, and to see God as He really is. Salvation comes by faith in God's grace through Jesus Christ, who promises to be with us no matter what may come. We can claim His free gift of eternal life, and His power for living, in an act of faith, by declaring God's promises found in the Bible. Salvation does not depend our works or feelings, but upon God alone.

Though our salvation is secure, every Christian needs to be refreshed by the good news of Jesus Christ every day, for we all fall short daily. Confession plays a part in this. A believer's confession does not reestablish one's salvation, but it can realign our thoughts and actions with God's purposes.

I used to feel different from other people, doubting that God's love really extended to me, but now I know that the quantum waves that make up my mind and soul are no different than those in any other human being. We are all made of the same atoms. Each soul arises from the same kinds of entangled quantum interactions within the body and brain. Because of this, and by the equivalence of observers, I know that I am intrinsically no different than anyone else. It is the same for you.

Each of us can be sure of God's promise of eternal life, even if we feel different than others, or unworthy, or removed from God. If God accepts anyone on the basis of what Christ has done, He will accept you and He will accept me. No one is so sinful that God cannot save them.

Jesus said, "This is the will of my Father, that everyone who looks on the Son and believes in Him should have eternal life."[54] If you believe in Jesus Christ, whom God sent to live among us, and as Paul wrote, "if you confess with your mouth that Jesus is Lord and believe in your heart that God raised Him from the dead, you will be saved."[55] It is as simple as that. We cannot save ourselves with any amount of effort or fretting.

The love of Jesus is a selfless kind of love, which He gives even if it is not reciprocated. This is the kind of love He wants from us. As John wrote, "We love because He first loved us."[56] This kind of love arises from a choice to love and act accordingly. If we ask for God's Spirit, He will transform us and make us able to forgive and give unconditional love to others.

Jesus experienced all the trials, temptations and joys in the flesh that we all face. God suffered for us in the person of Christ, He suffers with us now through entanglement, and He is always there to comfort us. He loves us more than we can know, and He alone is the answer to our suffering. Surely, He who gave up His Son for us will not withhold His love from us, or life in His heavenly home.[57]

FINDING GOD IN SCIENCE - QED

Astonishingly, the principles of entanglement and teleportation, Divinely established from the foundation of the universe, would appear to be the basis of Christianity. In this, Christianity is entirely unique.

Critics will say that what I have proposed is not provable, and that the similarities of quantum mechanics with Christ's message and mission are coincidences. However, the odds argue against such a chance correlation of the core tenets of Christianity, and the principles of quantum physics. To the contrary, the scientific evidence for God's existence and Christianity is stunning in its breadth.

The extreme fine tuning of physical laws implies that the configuration of nature did not come about by chance, but was selected by a Creator. The favorable conditions for life on Earth, as compared with the other known planets, suggest that we inhabit a truly blessed and remarkable planet, an island of sentient beings created in the likeness of God. The consistency of the Bible with science is another extraordinary validation of God's supernatural revelation.

It follows from the uncertainty principle that we have free will, and that God is the author of human freedom, even though He pre-selected everything that will occur from the foundation of the universe. In this way even the outcomes of purely random events are under His ultimate control. God sees the beginning from the end, and He may select the outcome of chance events to engineer outcomes and species, in the stream of time. Therefore, atheistic arguments against God based on chance events—arguments that chance eliminates design—are shown to be ill conceived.

Their arguments are wrong on at least three other counts. First, no one knows how the universe came to be in the first place. Secondly, finely tuned physical laws are the same as design in the universe—the design that atheists deny. Thirdly, all the time in the universe is not enough for life to arise by chance. Science has been unable to prove that multiple universes exist, but even if they do exist it seems unlikely that life could arise in any one of them entirely by chance. It takes as much faith to believe that unseen universes solve the problem of life arising by chance, as to believe in God. As imposing as the atheistic arguments based in chance seemed to me as a younger man, they are refuted by these truths.

The Father, Son and Holy Spirit, who are one, created a universe where relationship is the norm. It is a universe where atoms naturally unify to form the material world, and tiny entangled particles share information over any distance.

Quantum entanglement suggests that there is more to the universe than mere material. Most likely, quantum interactions are the basis of life itself. Almost certainly, the protomentality that arises during quantum interactions forms the basis of human consciousness. The grand quantum computation carried on by the universe also points to a Divine author of vast intellect.

Entanglement of the human will with the physical world makes us co-creators of the stream of history with God. Indeed, the role of the observer in quantum mechanics implies that there is little justification for seeing a stand-alone universe without a Super Observer—the Creator.

The parallel between quantum entanglement, and Christ's claim to indwell each believer is undeniable. The transfer of exact spiritual states, sin from believers to Christ, is not just a curious Christian idea, but it is exactly analogous to the new wonder of teleportation. This is not to say that all the mysteries of God have now been explained. It is quite impossible for anyone confined to time and space to really comprehend God, or His ways, but a Divine premeditation has been revealed that no human being could have expected.

The gospel has been reframed in a modern language, and one that has a direct correspondence with the most fundamental principles of physics. This does not change anything about the gospel, or add to the Bible, but, in a Divine surprise, evidence from modern science has authenticated key aspects of what Jesus did and said. He declared, "No one has ever seen God. The only Son, who is the same as God and is at the Father's side, He has made him known."[58] Jesus Christ has made God known to us in a way that harmonizes with what we now know from science, and He tells us how to be saved.

We can trust Christ when He says He has already overcome evil, and that we will be with Him in eternity.[59] His sacrificial love can bring us into fellowship with God in spite of any shortcoming, or anything that we have said, or done.

God loves you and wants to share life with you! If you do not yet know Him, talk to a follower of Jesus, or speak with a Christian pastor. Talk to God. Ask Him to make Himself known to you. Admit your failings, and tell Him that you want Him to transform you in the way that secures your spirit for God's pleasure. Let Him know that you want to have a relationship with Him, to really know and love Him. He is waiting for you to taste and see that God is good.

There can be no greater joy than this.

APPENDIX A: CORRELATING THE BIBLE & SCIENCE

There was a beginning of the universe	Genesis 1:1
The universe was void and empty at the beginning	Genesis 1:2
Information is a primary foundation of the universe	Psalm 33:6, John 1:1
God is not a part of the universe. Ironically many say they do not believe because God is not detectable in the universe.	Genesis 1:1
Early liquid universe after big bang[1] (quark-gluon plasma)	Genesis 1:2
Light was the first substance to come into existence	Genesis 1:3
Light was separated from dark when the universe became transparent (quark containment theory)	Genesis 1:4
Stars as innumerable as the sands of the sea	Hebrews 11:12
Planets, the Moon and stars differ, one from another	1 Corinthians 15:41
The heavens were stretched out, and still are stretching out	Jeremiah 51:15
Vast scope of the heavens (156 billion light years across)	Genesis 1:16-17
Heavens were created first then the Earth	Genesis 1:8 then 1:10
Seas are approximately as old as the Earth	Genesis 1:9, 10

Transparent atmosphere makes Stars, Sun and Moon visible from Earth	Genesis 1:14
The fixed order of heaven and Earth: unchanging natural laws	Jeremiah 33:25
Primal dust as the basis of worlds	Proverbs 8:26
Earth having a circular form	Proverbs 8:27, Isaiah 40:22, Job 26:10
The Earth is a privileged planet—a good place	Genesis 1:10
A dew watered the ground before rain, long before man and plants	Genesis 2:6
Water from the heavens, and comets, form the oceans of Earth	Genesis 1:6-10
Water cycle accurately described long before modern science	Psalm 135:6-7, Job 36:27-28, Jeremiah 10:13
Rain occurs before plants and trees	Genesis 2:5
Rain occurs before man appears	Genesis 2:5
Plants arise before animals	Genesis 1:11
Plants arise before man	Genesis 1:11
Seas abound with abundance of life (Cambrian explosion)	Genesis 1:20
Sea animals preceded land animals	Genesis 1:11
Earth and seas bring forth life forms in stages, describing evolution	Genesis 1:11, 20, 24
Flying animals (first insects) preceded larger land animals	Genesis 1:20

Genetic stability of life forms (stable DNA replication)	Genesis 1:11, 21, 25
Dinosaurs mentioned—taninim gedolim —the big reptiles[2]	Genesis 1:21, Exodus 7:10, 15
The archaeopteryx—the tinshemet — part reptile, part bird[3]	Leviticus 11:18, 30
Animals arise before man	Genesis 1:20, 24
Rabbits eat some of their own droppings and so 'chew the cud'	Deuteronomy 14:7
Human predecessors, chimps, have 13 sets of ribs while humans have 12	Genesis 2:21-23
Massive flooding in Mesopotamia—face of the aretz (earth), not the adamah (planet)[4]	Genesis 6
Relativity of time prefigured in scripture	Psalm 90:4-5
Comets and Asteroids accurately described before modern knowledge	Revelation 8:7-10
Increased knowledge and travel predicted	Daniel 12: 4
An end of the Earth by fire is foretold (consumed by the Sun)	2 Peter 3:7, Luke 21:33
An end of the heavens is foretold	Mark 13:31, Luke 21:33
Hell is a place of utter darkness and separation exists that nothing can escape, similar to Black Holes	Luke 16:25,26
The key aspects of Christianity were laid down when quantum mechanics was formulated by the Creator	Revelation 13: 8

The phenomenon of entanglement mirrors the act of Christ living within each person who believes and trusts Him	John 15:1-8
Entanglement mirrors the continuous communion of the Father, Son & Holy Spirit	John 10:30
Entanglement shows how Jesus Christ, as a man could remain in direct contact with the power of the Godhead	Matthew 17:2
Destruction of the original in teleportation implies Christ had to die to take away our sins	Mark 14:36, Luke 22:42, Acts 4:12
Teleportation implies we have to die to receive the fullness of His righteousness, in eternal life	Philippians 3:12

Notes:

1. NATURE, published online: 19 April 2005; Mark Peplow, doi:10.1038/news050418-5

2. The Science of God, Gerald L. Schroeder, Free Press, New York, NY, 1997, p. 193.

3. The Science of God, Gerald L. Schroeder, Free Press, New York, NY, 1997, p. 95.

4. Commentators have convincingly argued, from scripture, for a vast regional flood in the region of Eden rather than a planet wide flood. The Science of God, Gerald L. Schroeder, Free Press, New York, NY, 1997, ISBN 0-7679-0303-X, p. 205.

APPENDIX B: GLOSSARY OF TERMS

ASTEROID

An aggregate of rocky clumps of planetary debris and/ or iron. Asteroids can be as large as a mountain range, or even a planetoid like Vesta (a small planet).

ATOM

A unique arrangement of protons, neutrons and electrons that form the various elements like oxygen, iron, and uranium (etc.).

BEAM SPLITTER

A piece of glass, or crystal, that reflects a percentage of the incident photons, and transmits the rest. Beam splitters create entangled photons and are probably entangled with those photons.

BELL STATE MEASUREMENT

A Bell State Measurement is an operation that measures joint properties of an entangled pair, or group of particles, without finding the properties of the individual particles.

BLACK HOLE

A black hole is the remnant of a massive star (10 solar masses or more) that has collapsed to a city-sized volume.

BLUE SHIFT

A color shift in light toward the blue end of the light spectrum that can be used to determine how fast a distant star is moving toward the Earth.

BOHR'S CORRESPONDENCE PRINCIPLE

The classical world of Newtonian physics is a special case of quantum physics.

BROWN DWARF

A class of dark planetary body that is too small to sustain nuclear fusion.

BYTE OR BIT
The smallest possible unit of information in computing, represented by either a 0 or a 1. By contrast, a qubit is in two states at once (0 and 1), and a qubit may be entangled with other qubits.

CEPHEID STAR
The pulsing rate and intrinsic brightness of Cepheid stars allow them to be used as a reference stellar candle for deep space distance measurements.

CLASSICAL MECHANICS
A deterministic mathematical description of the motion of ordinary objects – velocity and position.

CLASSICAL WORLD
The commonly experienced behavior of ordinary objects and events described by Classical Mechanics.

COHERENCE
The state of entanglement, or degree of entanglement, among particles or objects.

COMET
A planetary body combination of water ice and rocky material. Comets can be as large as a mountain range.

CORRELATED STATE
Quantum states of entangled particles are always correlated, like a matching pair.

COSMIC BACKGROUND RADIATION
An ubiquitous primordial remnant of the initial radiation burst of the creation of the universe.

COSMOLOGICAL CONSTANT
A constant in Einstein's general relativity that describes the expansion of the volume of space of the universe.

COSMOLOGICAL SINGULARITY
The tiny point where space and time began 13.7 billion years ago – the beginning of the universe.

DARK ENERGY
Dark energy has been pushing the galaxies of the universe further apart, and its force has been getting stronger with time, making it the most abundant thing in the universe.

DARK MATTER
A strange non standard material that is significantly more plentiful than normal matter, comprising most of the material universe.

DECOHERENCE
The classical state of objects, and particles – ostensibly having no quantum entanglement. The bumping of atoms and molecules is enough to cause decoherence.

DELAYED CHOICE EXPERIMENT
A two slit light experiment where the choice to measure or not to measure passing photons is delayed to the last possible stage. The delayed choice changes the outcome of events that have already occurred within the test setup.

DETECTOR
A device that registers the passing of a particle or photon.

DETERMINISM
Everything that occurs is determined, according to this theory, by what occurred before, through physics. Strict determinism does not exist on the smallest scales.

DNA
The stable genetic instruction set that nature uses to construct, or grow, all the various known life forms.

DUAL NATURE
Light's particle and wave dual natures are called complementary properties. They both exist, even as they seem to contradict each other.

ELECTRICAL CHARGE
The electron has a negative charge while the proton has a positive charge. Stable atoms are electrically neutral, having the same number of protons and electrons.

ENTANGLEMENT
The instantaneous sharing of information among particles, or objects, over any distance without sending a signal. One byte of information is created out of nothing, when particles become entangled. Measurable physical characteristics are shared among entangled particles, as if they were a matched set, in correlated states. But, the state of neither particle is decided until one of them is measured.

GALAXY
A massive collection of stars, similar to the Sun, bound by a mutual gravitational force into a giant cluster. Typically, a great gap of empty space separates one galaxy from another, though galaxy mergers are common in the heavens.

GENERAL THEORY OF RELATIVITY
This describes gravity as the distortion of space by massive bodies. The larger the mass of an object, or planet, or star, the greater is the local distortion of space and the corresponding gravitational pull.

HABITABLE ZONE
The region of space around a star where conditions are favorable to life.

HUBBLE SPACE TELESCOPE
A large Earth orbiting space telescope that is not impeded by the detrimental effects of the atmosphere and city lights.

INDETERMINATE, OR NON-DETERMINATE
An outcome that is not fully constrained by its initial conditions. The same cause results in different outcomes in non determinate systems.

INFLATION
A period of rapid expansion of the very young universe that set the stage for the current enormity of the universe.

INTERFERENCE
Light waves can add (constructive interference) or cancel (destructive interference). Any type of wave can add, or cancel, in this manner leading to interference.

KELVIN
A scientific temperature scale, where 0 degrees Kelvin is the lowest possible temperature, where molecular motion is said to stop.

LIGHT YEAR
The distance that light travels in one Earth year – approximately 6 trillion miles (10 trillion kilometers).

LOCALITY
The direct action of a force on an object, as the only means of bringing about a change of speed, or direction of motion, of that object.

MAGNETOSPHERE
A magnetic "deflector shield" formed by planet's rotating magnetic field. The magnetosphere protects the planet and its atmosphere from energetic charged particles from space. Stars also have huge magnetospheres.

MEASUREMENT PROBLEM
Heisenberg's orthodox interpretation of the Schrödinger wave equation that a photon (or electron, or an atom) in isolation, has no definite location or velocity until a measurement is made. The observer becomes an integral part of the experiment in quantum physics.

MULTIVERSE
A theoretical nearly infinite set of universes that physically manifest all the possible quantum states for the 1090 elementary particles in this universe.

NEBULA
A collection of planetary gas and dust in space, ejected from earlier generation stars that have expended their nuclear fuel. The material in nebula is a source of star and planet formation.

NEUTRINO ENERGY FIELD
Energy derived from neutrino particles, which interacts very little with normal matter.

NON LOCAL
Quantum particles can behave in a non local fashion, that is, they can be influenced without direct physical action, or the sending of a signal. Entangled particles share information over any distance instantaneously. Processes governed by non locality.

ORTHODOX COPENHAGEN INTERPRETATION
Quantum physics holds that the true behavior of atomic particle and light is inherently non deterministic. The instantaneous sharing of information by particles at any distance—non locality—is a key prediction of this interpretation of quantum physics. The role of an observer in physical outcomes is also implied in this interpretation.

PHOTON
A particle or packet of light. Light also behaves with wave properties.

PLANCK TIME
The smallest theoretical division of time, 10^{-43} seconds.

PLASMA
A hot ionized form of matter, where some of the electrons have been stripped off the material's atoms by intense heat, as in the Sun.

PLATE TECTONICS
The various sections of the Earth's crust move over the planet's molten core, producing the continents, mountains and volcanoes.

POSTMODERNISM
The view that there is no real truth and that whatever benefits the state is the truth.

POTENTIA
The potential for an outcome that is said to be the true state of unmeasured particles.

PROBABILITY FUNCTION
An equation describing the probability of finding a particle in a certain place, or with a certain velocity.

PROTOMENTALITY
A basic proto consciousness associated with every quantum event.

QED (WHICH WAS TO BE DEMONSTRATED)
It is used here with a double meaning since QED also stands for Quantum Electrodynamics.

QUANTUM
Mass, energy, space and time are quantized, existing in tiny discreet units at the smallest scales, rather than being infinitely divisible into smaller and smaller units.

QUANTUM COMPUTER
A computer that uses switches that can be both open and closed at the same time, meaning the switches are entangled. Quantum computers can solve some problems that are impossible for classical computers, and are faster for other kinds of problems.

QUANTUM MECHANICS, OR QUANTUM PHYSICS
The description of the interactions of matter and energy at the smallest scales—atomic particles.

QUANTUM MIND THEORY
Consciousness arises in human beings in conjunction with entangled electron transfers from synapse to synapse. As electrons "tunnel" across the brain, they form electron waves that interconnect the various parts of the brain so that information is shared across the span of the brain.

QUANTUM PHENOMENA
Interactions of mass, energy, space, and time that are quantized and discreet at the smallest scales.

QUANTUM TUNNELING
Occurs, for instance, when a particle escapes from an atom's nuclear binding energy, without having all the energy required to "jump" that barrier.

QUARK-GLUON PLASMA
A super hot liquid with a very low viscosity, and is so uniform that it looks the same from any angle. A form of material in the early universe.

QUBIT
The smallest unit of quantum computing information. A qubit is in two states at once (0 and 1) and a qubit may be entangled with other qubits.

RED DWARF STAR
A dim star with only a fraction of the mass of the Sun.

RED SHIFT
A color shift in light toward the red end of the light spectrum that can be used to determine how fast a distant star is moving away from the Earth.

SCHR&DINGER WAVE EQUATION
Describes what may occur in a system of quantum particles when an experiment—a measurement—is performed on that system. Outcomes are described as probabilities (probability function or wave potential).

SOLAR SYSTEM
The system of planets to which the Earth belongs, with the Sun at its center. The solar system orbits the center of the Milky Way galaxy, which in turn orbits within a local galaxy group. Numerous other similar star systems have been discovered.

SPECIAL THEORY OF RELATIVITY
The speed of light is the same for all observers, whatever their location or velocity. Time's passage slows down, or dilates, on a rocket as it gets closer to the speed of light.

SPECTROMETER
An instrument for measuring the energy/ frequency content of light.

STATE VECTOR COLLAPSE
When an outcome of a measurement has been selected, the Schrödinger wave equation is said to "collapse" to just one of the possible outcomes.

SUPER NOVA
An exploding star that has reached the end of its nuclear fuel and the end of its useful life as a star.

SUPERPOSITION OF STATES
A particle or an ensemble of particles that exist in two states at once. All waves naturally superimpose themselves through the addition and subtraction of the overlapping wave's amplitudes.

TELEPORTATION
Traveling without moving. An object is teleported through a process of destructive Bell state measurement that produces a three way entanglement. This makes it possible to recreate an exact copy of the original object at a remote location.

TIDAL LOCKING
Occurs when the same side of a planetary body always faces its host world. The same side of the Moon always faces the Earth due to the gravitational gradient between the two bodies.

TIME DILATION
Time slows down more and more as a clock on a rocket accelerates closer to the speed of light.

TIME INVARIANCE
The result of a quantum measurement is unchanged no matter when an observer looks, and no matter how many observers look. Certain delayed choice measurements also seem to upset the temporal scheme of cause and effect.

TWO SLIT EXPERIMENT
Light is made to pass through two slits in a plate and is projected onto a screen a bit further from the light source than the plate with the slits. The light that passes through the slits produces a pattern of light and dark on the screen through wave interference.

UNCERTAINTY PRINCIPLE
The velocity or position of small particles can be described with high precision, but not both. A close knowledge of one parameter necessarily means uncertainty in the other.

UNIVERSE
The totality of time, space, and all energy and material contained by them. Our universe is 13.7 billion years old and about 156 light years across.

ZERO POINT FIELD
Empty space is actually full of transient energy as described by the uncertainty principle.

APPENDIX C: CITATIONS & BIBLIOGRAPHY

Author's Preface: Why Finding God?

1. 1 Corinthians 13:11, English Standard Version.
2. Erwin Schrödinger, 'What is Life' with 'Mind and Matter' and Autobiographical Sketches', Cambridge University Press, ISBN 978-0-521-42708-1, 1992.
3. Antony Flew with Roy Abraham Varghese, There Is A God, Harper One, New York, New York, 2007, ISBN 978-0-06-133530-3, p. 89.
4. Stephen Hawking, A Brief History of Time, Bantam Books, New York, NY, 1988, ISBN 0-553-05340-X, p. 175.

Chapter 1: Why Should I Care About Science?

1. Allister E. McGrath, 'To Capture the Imagination of Our Culture: Reflections on Christian Apologetics,' An edited version of Alistair McGrath's inaugural address as Director of the Oxford Centre for Evangelism.
2. Lee Smolin, Three Roads to Quantum Gravity, 2001, Published by Basic Books, First published in Great Britain 2000 by Weidenfeld and Nicolson. ISBN 0-465-07836-2, p. 17.
3. Pravda editors, Yuri Gagarin's smile remains symbol of space exploration era for almost 50 years, Pravda.ru, 09.03.2009, accessed October, 2011. http://english.pravda.ru/history/09-03-2009/107206-gagarin-0/
4. John 7:7, New King James Version.
5. Daniel M. Abrams and Haley A. Yaple and Richard J. Wiener, 'A mathematical model of social group competition with application to the growth of religious non-affiliation,' Department of Engineering Sciences and Applied Mathematics, Northwestern University, Evanston, Illinois 60208, USA and Research Corporation for Science Advancement, Tucson, Arizona and Department of Physics, University of Arizona, Tucson, Arizona, Dated: January 17, 2011.m and Apologetics, delivered in February 2005, p. 4.
6. Fred Heeren, Show Me God, Day Star Publications, Wheeling, IL, 1998, ISBN 1-885849-52-4, p. 334.
7. Francis S. Collins, The Language of God, Free Press Simon and Schuster, Inc., New York, 2006, ISBN 978-0-7432-8639-8, p. 58

8. 1 Corinthians 2:5, New King James Version.
9. Romans 14:14, English Standard Version.
10. Psalm 19:2-3, New King James Version.
11. Isaiah 43:19, English Standard Version.
12. Gautam Naik, Mistakes in Scientific Studies Surge, Dow Jones & Company, a division of News Corporation, New York, Wednesday, August 10, 2011.
13. James Taylor – Managing Editor Of Environment & Climate News, Chilling Thoughts For Global-Warming Alarmists, Forbes Publishing, New York, 11.16.11, 06:00 PM EST, Forbes Magazine dated December 05, 2011. http://www.forbes.com/forbes/2011/1205/opinions-capital-flows-global-warming-alarmists- james-taylor.html
14. Kate Ravilious, Mars Melt Hints at Solar, Not Human, Cause for Warming, Scientist Says, National Geographic News, February 28, 2007. Accessed 11/18/2012. http://news.nationalgeographic.com/news/2007/02/070228-mars-warming.html
15. Marlowe Hood, Global Warming Hits Mars Too, Mars Daily, Agence France-Presse, Paris, Apr 06, 2007. Accessed 11/18/2012. http://www.marsdaily.com/reports/Global_Warming_Hits_Mars_Too_999.html
16. Jason Palmer, Science and technology reporter, Palm Trees 'Grew on Antarctica', BBC News, 1 August 2012. https://www.bbc.com/news/science-environment-19077439, accessed September 19, 2020.
Also see, Laura Geggel, Remains of 90 million-year-old rainforest discovered under Antarctic ice, published April 02, 2020, https://www.livescience.com/ancient-rainforest-antarctica.html, accessed August 5, 2023.
Also see, CBS News, X-SCITECH, Study: North Pole Once Was Tropical , First published on May 31, 2006 / 3:53 PM
© 2006 The Associated Press. All Rights Reserved. This material may not be published, broadcast, rewritten, or redistributed.
17. Kevin Krajick, Fossil leaves show high atmospheric carbon spurred ancient 'global greening,' Earth Institute at Columbia University, August 20, 2020, accessed September 15, 2020.
https://www.sciencedaily.com/releases/2020/08/200820102444.htm
18. Matt Ridley, Climate Change Will Not Be Dangerous for a Long Time, November 27, 2015. Accessed December 7, 2015. http://www.scientificamerican.com/article/climate-change-will-not-be-dangerous-for -a-long- time/

19. Andrew Orlowski, Top Boffin Freeman Dyson on Climate Change, Interstellar Travel, Fusion, and More, The Register, October 11, 2015. Accessed December 18, 2015. http://www.theregister.co.uk/2015/10/11/freeman_dyson_interview/
20. Nathan Worcester, 7/29/2023, 'We Are Totally Awash in Pseudoscience': Nobel Prize-Winning Physicist on Climate Agenda, His speech 'postponed' by the IMF, John Clauser speaks out, Epoch Times Updated: 8/1/2023, Accessed 8/1/2023 https://www.theepochtimes.com/mkt_app/us/exclusive-we-are-totally-awash-in-pseudoscience-nobel-prize-winning-physicist-on-climate-agenda-5430650?src_src=Morningbrief&src_cmp=mb-2023-08-01&est=IAKFf3uB7whnFcOIFx8h%2B72nIZS0oKYU8pcjKYVcSCRl4JpYBLlV8yoPfycQ3A%3D%3D
21. Proverbs 25:2, English Standard Version.
22. Hosea 4:6, New King James Version.
23. John 20:27, English Standard Version.
24. Daniel 12:4, English Standard Version.
25. Matthew 10: 16, English Standard Version.
26. John H. Walton, The Lost World of Genesis One, InterVarsity Press, Downers Grove, Illinois, 2009, page 113.
27. Francis A. Schaeffer, Escape From Reason, Inter-Varsity Press, 1968, 130 North Wells, Chicago, Illinois 60606 Library of Congress Catalog Card Number 68-58084, p. 21.
28. 1 Corinthians 15:40-41, English Standard Version.
29. Stephen Lang, What The Bible Did Not Say, Fall River Press, New York, New York, 2003 ISBN -13: 978-1-4351-0594-2, p. 90.
30. Stephen Hawking, A Brief History of Time, Bantam Books, New York, NY, 1988, ISBN 0-553-05340-X, p. 16.
31. Dan Hofstadler, The Earth Moves: Galileo and the Roman Inquisition, W. W. Norton & Company, New York, New York, 2009 ISBN -13: 978-0-393-06650-0, p. 196.
32. 1 Chronicles 16:29-30, New International Version.
33. Pope John Paul II, Message To The Pontifical Academy Of Sciences: On Evolution, Message delivered to the Pontifical Academy of Sciences 22 October 1996 in Rome.
34. Nicole Winfield, Vatican: Faithful should listen to science, USA Today, Posted 11/3/2005 7:05 pm, The Associated Press. http://www.usatoday.com/tech/science/ethics/2005-11-03-vatican-science_x.htm

35. Pontifical Academy of Sciences, Wikipedia web site, accessed 9/28/2010. http://en.wikipedia.org/wiki/Pontifical_Academy_of_Sciences#Current_ordinary_members,
36. 2 Corinthians 13:8, English Standard Version.
37. Ann Spangler, Praying the Names of God, Zondervan, Grand Rapids Michigan 49530, 2004, ISBN 0-310-25353-5, p. 304.

Chapter 2: The Glory In The Heavens

1. Hebrews 11:12, New King James Version.
2. Hugh Ross Ph. D, Genesis One: A Scientific Perspective, Wisemen Productions, 40 S. Hermosa, Sierra Madre, CA 91024, p. 1.
3. Psalm 147:4, English Standard Version.
4. Jeremiah 51:15, English Standard Version.
5. John Hawley, Katherine Holcomb, Foundations of Modern Cosmology, Second Edition, Oxford University Press, New York, 2005. P. 284
6. John Hawley, Katherine Holcomb, Foundations of Modern Cosmology, Second Edition, Oxford University Press, New York, 2005. P. 288.
7. Mario Livio, The Accelerating Universe, John Wiley & Sons, Inc., 2000, New York, NY, ISBN 0-471-32969-X, p. 163, p. 127.
8. N. Smith, J. A. Morse, et al. of the University of Colorado, Eta Carinae and the Homunculus Nebula, Astronomy Picture of the Day, GSFC, NASA, 2008 June 17. http://antwrp.gsfc.nasa.gov/apod/ap080617.html, accessed 8/31/2010.
9. Luke 16:25-26, English Standard Version.
10. Karl Stapelfeldt and Paul Kalas, Hubble Directly Observes a Planet Orbiting Another Star, November 13, 2008, NASA's Jet Propulsion Laboratory, Pasadena, California.
11. Irene Klotz, Earth-Like Planet Can Sustain Life, Located in a solar system that parallels our own, the new world could be habitable — or even inhabited, Wed Sep 29, 2010 05:01 PM ET http://news.discovery.com/space/earth-like-planet-life.html
12. Whitney Clavin, NASA's Kepler Mission Discovers Two Planets Transiting Same Star, August 26, 2010. Accessed September 30, 2011. http://www.jpl.nasa.gov/news/news.cfm?release=2010-279, accessed 8/27/2010.

Chapter 3: The Earth, Genesis & Civilization

1. Isaiah 40:22, New Living Translation.
2. Proverbs 8:27, English Standard Version.
3. Planetary information from http://www.jpl.nasa.gov/missions/ or Wikipedia, except as noted.
4. Genesis 1:14-19, New King James Version.
5. Gerald L. Schroeder, The Science of God, Free Press, New York, NY, 1997, ISBN 0-7679-0303-X, p. 67.
6. Hugh Ross Ph. D, Genesis One: A Scientific Perspective, Wisemen Productions, 40 S. Hermosa, Sierra Madre, CA 91024, p. 9.
7. Paul Voosen, World's oldest ice core could solve mystery of 'flipped' ice age cycles, 30 Oct 2019, accessed October 27, 2022. https://www.science.org/content/article/world-s-oldest-ice-core-could-solve-mystery-flipped-ice-age-cycles
8. Kenneth Miller, Finding Darwin's God, A Scientist's Search for Common Ground Between God and
Evolution, Cliff Street Books, An Imprint of Harper Collins Publishers, NY, NY, copyright 1999, ISBN 0-06-017593-1, p. 71-72
9. George R. Tilton and Clair Cameron Patterson, 1922—1995, A Biographical Memoir, National Academies Press, Washington D.C., Copyright 1998, p. 7.
10. Hugh Ross Ph. D, Genesis One: A Scientific Perspective, Wisemen Productions, 40 S. Hermosa, Sierra Madre, CA 91024, p. 11.
11. Gleason L. Archer, Encyclopedia of Bible Difficulties, Zondervan Corporation, Grand Rapids, Michigan, 1982, ISBN 0-310-43570-6, p. 60-61.
12. Gerald L. Schroeder, The Science of God, Free Press, New York, NY, 1997, ISBN 0-7679-0303-X, p. 97.
13. Psalm 90, 3-6, New King James Version.
14. Fred Heeren, Show Me God, Day Star Publications, Wheeling, IL, 1998, ISBN 1-885849-52-4, p. 187
15. Genesis 2:16:17 and Genesis 5:5, King James Version.
16. Genesis 2:4 and Genesis 5:1, King James Version.
17. Psalm 135:6-7, New King James Version.
18. Job 36:27, New King James Version.
19. Francis S. Collins, The Language of God, Free Press Simon and Schuster, Inc., New York, 2006, ISBN 978-0-7432-8639-8, p. 200.
20. David Frost, Billy Graham, Personal Thoughts of a Public Man, 30 Years of Conversations with David Frost, Chariot Victor Publishing, a

division of Cook Communications, Colorado Springs, ISBN 0-7814-1545-4, 1997, p. 73-74.
21. C.S. Lewis, The Problem of Pain, Harper Collins, New York, New York, 1996, pg. 77.
22. Genesis 2:7, Genesis 1:11, Genesis 1:12, Genesis 1:24, English Standard Version.
23. Mark 4:26-28, New King James Version.
24. Jewish Virtual Library, A Project Of AICE, https://www.jewishvirtuallibrary.org/the-blessing-over-bread-hamotzi, accessed 8/4/2023.
25. Romans 8:29, New King James Version.
26. Genesis 2:7 King James Version, and Gerald L. Schroeder, The Science of God, Free Press, New York, NY, 1997, ISBN 0-7679-0303-X, p. 117.
27. Gerald L. Schroeder, The Science of God, Free Press, New York, NY, 1997, ISBN 0-7679- 0303- X, p. 117, 145.
28. Gleason L. Archer, Encyclopedia of Bible Difficulties, Zondervan Corporation, Grand Rapids, Michigan, 1982, ISBN 0-310-43570-6, p. 64.
29. John 4: 24 and Genesis 2: 7, English Standard Version.
30. Philippians 2:6-7, English Standard Version.
31. Psalms 17:15, New King James Version.
32. Job 38:4, New King James Version.
33. Genesis 1:13, New King James Version.
34. New Scientist Editors, Sluggish reptile evolving at record speed, Reed Business Information Ltd, United Kingdom, March 2008, p. 17.
Journal Reference; Trends in Genetics, DOI: 10.1016/j.tig.2007.12.002
http://www.newscientist.com/article/mg19726495.000-sluggish-reptile-evolving-at-record- speed.html
35. Jerome F. Hamlin, Coelacanth Information, The Fish Out of Time, Third Wave Media Incorporated, ©2011, 10/13/11, Accessed October 13, 2011. http://www.dinofish.com/
36. Frank J. Tipler, The Physics Of Christianity, Doubleday, New York, NY, 2007, ISBN 978-0-385-51424-8 p. 189.
37. Walking fish, http://en.wikipedia.org/wiki/Walking_fish, accessed October 13, 2011.
38. Hugh Ross, More Than A Theory, Baker Books, Grand Rapids, MI 2009, ISBN 978-0-8010-1327-0, p. 152, 139.
39. Seth Lloyd, Programming The Universe, Vintage Books, Random House Inc. New York, New York 2007. ISBN: 978-1-4000-3386-7, p. 57.
40. Proverbs 25:2, English Standard Version.

41. David Rohl, From Eden to Exile, The 5000-Year History of the People of the Bible, GreenLeaf Press, Lebanon, Tennessee, ISBN 1-882514-58-0, 2009 p. 19-24, 38-39.
42. Richard James Fischer, Historical Genesis, University Press of America, Inc., 4501 Forbes Boulevard, Suite 200, Lanham, Maryland 20706, ISBN-13: 978-0-7618-3807-4, p. 38-42. Also see David Rohl, From Eden to Exile, The 5000-Year History of the People of the Bible, GreenLeaf Press, Lebanon, Tennessee, ISBN 1-882514-58-0, 2009 p. 202-203.
43. Richard James Fischer, Historical Genesis, University Press of America, Inc., 4501 Forbes Boulevard, Suite 200, Lanham, Maryland 20706, ISBN-13: 978-0-7618-3807-4, p. 40.
44. David Rohl, Legend, The Genesis of Civilisation, Butler & Tanner Ltd, Frome and London, 1998, ISBN 0 7126 7747 X, p. 54.
45. David Rohl, Legend, The Genesis of Civilisation, Butler & Tanner Ltd, Frome and London, 1998, ISBN 0 7126 7747 X, p. 66-67.
46. David Rohl, From Eden to Exile, The 5000-Year History of the People of the Bible, GreenLeaf Press, Lebanon, Tennessee, ISBN 1-882514-58-0, 2009, p. 31.
47. Genesis 4:14-16, New King James Version.
48. Genesis 4:17-18, New King James Version.
49. David Rohl, From Eden to Exile, The 5000-Year History of the People of the Bible, GreenLeaf Press, Lebanon, Tennessee, ISBN 1-882514-58-0, 2009, p. 35. And, David Rohl, Legend, The Genesis of Civilisation, Butler & Tanner Ltd, Frome and London, 1998, ISBN 0 7126 7747 X, p. 197-200.
50. Richard James Fischer, Historical Genesis, University Press of America, Inc., 4501 Forbes Boulevard, Suite 200, Lanham, Maryland 20706, ISBN-13: 978-0-7618-3807-4, p. 52-53.
51. Genesis 4: 21-22, New King James Version.
52. Genesis 2:16-17, New King James Version.
53. Richard James Fischer, Historical Genesis, University Press of America, Inc., 4501 Forbes Boulevard, Suite 200, Lanham, Maryland 20706, ISBN-13: 978-0-7618-3807-4, p. 26-27.
54. Charles Darwin, The Descent of Man and Selection in Relation to Sex, New York, Appleton and Co., 1883.723.
55. Romans 5:12, New King James Version.
56. 1 Corinthians 15:22, New King James Version.
57. Romans 8:20, New King James Version.
58. Genesis 3:19, New King James Version.

59. The Scofield Study Bible, New King James Version, Thomas Nelson Inc., Oxford University Press, New York, New York, 1982, 2002 edition, p. 13.
60. Gerald L. Schroeder, The Science of God, Free Press, New York, NY, 1997, ISBN 0-7679-0303-X, p. 205, 206.
61. Richard James Fischer, Historical Genesis, University Press of America, Inc., 4501 Forbes Boulevard, Suite 200, Lanham, Maryland 20706, ISBN-13: 978-0-7618-3807-4, p. 78, 96, 105.
62. Richard James Fischer, Historical Genesis, University Press of America, Inc., 4501 Forbes Boulevard, Suite 200, Lanham, Maryland 20706, ISBN-13: 978-0-7618-3807-4, p. 54-55.
63. Rich Deem, The Genesis Flood, Why the Bible Says It Must be Local, http://www.godandscience.org/apologetics/localflood.html, Accessed August 5, 2023.
64. Richard James Fischer and Don Perrett, Revised King James Version of Genesis 1-11, Genesis Proclaimed Association, PO Box 50111, Arlington, VA 22205, http://genesisproclaimed.org/Content/Detail/29, accessed August 29, 2023.
65. Genesis 4:14, New King James Version.
66. Exodus 10:15, New King James Version.
67. Rich Deem, The Genesis Flood, Why the Bible Says It Must be Local, http://www.godandscience.org/apologetics/localflood.html, Accessed August 5, 2023.
68. David Rohl, From Eden to Exile, The 5000-Year History of the People of the Bible, GreenLeaf Press, Lebanon, Tennessee, ISBN 1-882514-58-0, 2009, p.45-55.
69. Richard James Fischer, Historical Genesis, University Press of America, Inc., 4501 Forbes Boulevard, Suite 200, Lanham, Maryland 20706, ISBN-13: 978-0-7618-3807-4, p. 158.
70. Flavius Josephus, Antiquities of the Jews, Book 1, Chapter 3, Bible Study Tools on the Salem Web Network, copyright 2023, accessed July 11, 2023.
71. Richard James Fischer, Historical Genesis, University Press of America, Inc., 4501 Forbes Boulevard, Suite 200, Lanham, Maryland 20706, ISBN-13: 978-0-7618-3807-4, p. 125.
72. Numbers 13:33, New King James Version.
73. John 15:24, New King James Version.
74. Richard James Fischer, Historical Genesis, University Press of America, Inc., 4501 Forbes Boulevard, Suite 200, Lanham, Maryland 20706, ISBN-13: 978-0-7618-3807-4, p. 68.

75. Richard James Fischer and Don Perrett, Revised King James Version of Genesis 1-11, Genesis Proclaimed Association, PO Box 50111, Arlington, VA 22205, http://genesisproclaimed.org/Content/Detail/29, accessed August 29, 2023.
76. Richard James Fischer, Historical Genesis, University Press of America, Inc., 4501 Forbes Boulevard, Suite 200, Lanham, Maryland 20706, ISBN-13: 978-0-7618-3807-4, p. 54, 55.
77. Sean McDowell, Sodom & Gomorrah: The Evidence, Discovering the Lost City of Sodom with Dr. Steven Collins, https://www.youtube.com/watch?v=GkATIhRxxaE, accessed August 5, 2023.
78. Ted E. Bunch, et. al, A Tunguska sized airburst destroyed Tall el-Hammam a Middle Bronze Age city in the Jordan Valley near the Dead Sea, www.nature.com/scientificreports, 2011, accessed July 13, 2023.
79. Richard James Fischer, Historical Genesis, University Press of America, Inc., 4501 Forbes Boulevard, Suite 200, Lanham, Maryland 20706, ISBN-13: 978-0-7618-3807-4, p. 109-112.
80. Richard James Fischer, Historical Genesis, University Press of America, Inc., 4501 Forbes Boulevard, Suite 200, Lanham, Maryland 20706, ISBN-13: 978-0-7618-3807-4, p. 177.
81. Rich Deem, The Genesis Flood, Why the Bible Says It Must be Local, http://www.godandscience.org/apologetics/localflood.html, Accessed August 5, 2023.
82. Genesis 2: 4-6, New King James Version.
83. Genesis 6: 7, New King James Version.
84. Genesis 2:21-23, English Standard Version.
85. Michael Shermer, Why Darwin Matters: The Case Against Intelligent Design, Owl Books, Henry Holt and Company, New York, 2006, p.18.
86. Gerald L. Schroeder, The Science of God, Free Press, New York, NY, 1997, ISBN 0-7679-0303-X, p. 192-194.
87. Gerald L. Schroeder, The Science of God, Free Press, New York, NY, 1997, ISBN 0-7679-0303-X, p. 95-96.
88. Antony Flew with Roy Abraham Varghese, There Is A God, Harper One, New York, New York, 2007, ISBN 978-0-06-133530-3, p. 95.
89. Kent C. Condie, Plate Tectonics and Crustal Evolution, Butterworth – Heinemann, Burlington, MA, 1997, ISBN 0 7506 3386 7, p. 1, 6, 74- 77.
90. Clue To First Appearance Of Large Animals, Science Daily. Story is reprinted (with editorial adaptations by Science Daily staff) from materials provided by Queen's University. Retrieved July 12, 2011, from http://www.sciencedaily.com /releases/2006/12/061209083521.htm

91. Genesis 1:28, King James Version, and Genesis 9:1, King James Version.
92. David Whitehouse, BBC News Online science editor, Odds against Earth-like planets System', BBC, 28 January, 2003, accessed August 7, 2023, http://news.bbc.co.uk/2/hi/science/nature/2701977.stm

Chapter 4: To The Moon And Mars

1. Hugh Ross, More Than A Theory, Baker Books, Grand Rapids, MI 2009, ISBN 978-0-8010- 1327-0, p. 136.
2. Manuel Grande, SMART-1 on the trail of the Moon's beginnings, ESA News, D-CIXS Principal Investigator, University of Wales, Aberystwyth, UK, 18 August 2006.
3. Dr. Tony Phillips – editor, LCROSS Finds Water on the Moon, Credit: Science@NASA, November 13, 2009, accessed October 13, 2011. http://science.nasa.gov/science-news/science-at-nasa/2009/13nov_lcrossresults/
4. Psalms 89:37, New King James Version.
5. Nola Taylor Redd, SPACE.com Contributor, Percival Lowell Biography, Space.com, accessed 5/4/13 12:50 PM. http://www.space.com/19774-percival-lowell-biography.html
6. NASA Facts, National Aeronautics and Space Administration, Jet Propulsion Laboratory, California Institute of Technology Pasadena, CA 91109, 5-96 JHW.
7. Sara Hammond, Guy Webster, NASA Spacecraft Confirms Martian Water, Mission Extended, Phoenix Mars Lander, Exploring the Arctic Plain of Mars, July 31, 2008. http://www.nasa.gov/mission_pages/phoenix/news/phoenix-20080731.html
8. Guy Webster, NASA Spacecraft Data Suggest Water Flowing on Mars, Jet Propulsion Laboratory, Pasadena, Calif., accessed 5/4/13 12:55 PM http://www.nasa.gov/mission_pages/MRO/news/mro20110804.html
9. John Ruley, Simulation Shows Bacteria Could Live on Mars, Astrobiology Magazine, December 04, 2008, accessed 7.26.2013, – See more at: http://www.space.com/6191-simulation- shows-bacteria-live-mars.html#sthash.1Nv287N5.dpuf
10. Bill Steigerwald, Martian Methane Reveals the Red Planet is not a Dead Planet, Mars, NASA's Goddard Space Flight Center, NASA Explores the Red Planet, 15 January 15, 2009. http://www.nasa.gov/mission_pages/mars/news/marsmethane.html

11. Guy Webster, NASA Rover Finds Active and Ancient Organic Chemistry on Mars, JPL, California Institute of Technology, December 16, 2014. http://www.jpl.nasa.gov/news/news.php?feature=4413 – accessed Jan. 31, 2015, 9:31 PM.
12. Marcus Y. Woo, Roving On Mars, California Institute Of Technology Engineering & Science, Volume LXXII, Number 2, Fall 2009, pages 12-13.
13. Opportunity Update, Opportunity's Mission Is Complete, Sols 5347 to 5353, Feb. 7, 2019 - Feb. 13, 2019, accessed 3/24/2020. https://mars.nasa.gov/mer/mission/rover-status/
14. DC Agle, NASA Rover Finds Conditions Once Suited for Ancient Life on Mars, March 12, 2013, accessed 4/23/13 9:21 PM http://www.jpl.nasa.gov/news/news.php?release=2013-092

Chapter 5: Terrors And Great Signs

1. Luke 21:11, English Standard Version.
2. Preston Dyches, Cassini Finds Global Ocean in Saturn's Moon Enceladus, Jet Propulsion Laboratory, Pasadena, California, Sept. 15, 2015. https://www.nasa.gov/press/2014/april/nasa-space-assets-detect-ocean-inside-saturn- moon/ - accessed October 29, 2015.
3. Revelation 16:8, English Standard Version.
4. Mark Boslough and David Crawford, Frequently Asked Questions about the Collision of Comet Shoemaker-Levy 9 with Jupiter, astro@sfasu.edu, Last Updated on February 2, 1996. http://www.physics.sfasu.edu/astro/sl9/cometfaq2.html#Q3.1
5. Tariq Malik, Comet Dive-Bombs Sun During Big Solar Eruption, SPACE.com Managing Editor, 13 July 2011. http://www.space.com/11663-comet-hits-sun-solar -explosion.html Also, Tariq Malik, Comet's Death by Sun Photographed for First Time, SPACE.com Managing Editor, 12 May 2011. http://www.space.com/12250-comet-death-sun-photograph-spacecraft.html
6. Stephen Hawking, Only Space Travel Can Save Mankind, The Telegraph, 9 August 2010. http://www.telegraph.co.uk/science/space/7935355/Stephen-Hawking-only-space-travel- can-save-mankind.html, accessed 9/1/2010.
7. Revelation 8:8-11, English Standard Version.
8. Don Yeomans, Webmaster: Ron Baalke, Predicting Apophis' Earth Encounters in 2029 and 2036, last updated 30 Sep 2011.http://neo.jpl.nasa.gov/apophis/, accessed 9/30/2011.

9. Dr. Tony Phillips, What Exploded over Russia?, Science@NASA Headline News, Feb. 26, 2013, accessed 4/27/13 10:42 AM http://science.nasa.gov/science-news/science-at-nasa/2013/26feb_russianmeteor/
10. 2 Thessalonians 2:3, New King James Version.
11. Matthew 24:21-22, English Standard Version.

Chapter 6: A Beginning And An End Of All Things

1. Stephen Hawking, A Brief History of Time, Bantam Books, New York, NY, 1988, ISBN 0-553-05340-X, p. 46.
2. Professor Lamek Hulthén of the Royal Academy of Sciences, The Nobel Prize in Physics 1978, Pyotr Kapitsa, Arno Penzias, Robert Woodrow Wilson, Award Ceremony Speech Presentation Speech, Translation from the Swedish text http://nobelprize.org/nobel_prizes/physics/laureates/1978/presentation-speech.html
3. Webmaster Michael R. Greason, NASA Official Dr. Gary F. Hinshaw, Cosmic Background Explorer, page updated: Thursday, 26-Jun-2008. http://lambda.gsfc.nasa.gov/product/cobe/
4. Black Body, Wikipedia, http://en.wikipedia.org/wiki/Black_body, accessed July 17, 2011.
5. Webmaster: Britt Griswold, NASA Official: Dr. Gary F. Hinshaw 'Five Year Results on the Oldest Light in the Universe,' WMAP 5-year Results Released – March 7, 2008. http://map.gsfc.nasa.gov/news/5yr_release.html
6. David Schramm, ' Dark Matter and the Origin of Cosmic Structure,' Sky & Telescope, October, 1994, p. 29.
7. Webmaster: Michael R. Greason, NASA Official: Dr. Gary F. Hinshaw, Page Updated: Thursday, 26-Jun-2008, Cosmic Background Explorer. http://lambda.gsfc.nasa.gov/product/cobe/
8. Webmaster: Britt Griswold, NASA Official: Dr. Gary F. Hinshaw 'Five Year Results on the Oldest Light in the Universe,' WMAP 5-year Results Released – March 7, 2008. http://map.gsfc.nasa.gov/news/5yr_release.html
9. Fred Heeren, Show Me God, Day Star Publications, Wheeling, IL, 1998, ISBN 1-885849-52-4, p. 157.
10. Fred Heeren, Show Me God, Day Star Publications, Wheeling, IL, 1998, ISBN 1-885849-52-4, p. 157.
11. Hugh Ross, More Than A Theory, Baker Books, Grand Rapids, MI 2009, ISBN 978-0-8010-1327-0, p. 98.

12. Robert Jastrow, God and the Astronomers, second edition, New York & London: W.W. Norton & Company, 1992, p.14.
13. Job 9:8, New Living Testament.
14. Ann Spangler, Praying the Names of God, Zondervan, Grand Rapids Michigan 49530, 2004, ISBN 0-310-25353-5, p. 304.
15. Hugh Ross Ph. D, Genesis One: A Scientific Perspective, Wisemen Productions, 40 S. Hermosa, Sierra Madre, CA 91024, p. 19
16. Gerald L. Schroeder, The Science of God, Free Press, New York, NY, 1997, ISBN 0-7679-0303-X, p. 24.
17. David Lindley, Uncertainty, Einstein, Heisenberg, Bohr, and the Struggle for the Soul of Science, Doubleday, New York, 2007, ISBN 978-0-385-51506-1, p. 219
18. Stephen Hawking and Leonard Mlodinow, The Grand Design, Bantam Books, New York, NY, 2010, ISBN 978-0-553-80537-6, p. 180-183. Also see, Stephen Hawking: God did not create Universe, BBC News UK Online, 2 September 2010, Last updated at 18:25 ET, http://www.bbc.co.uk/news/uk-11172158, accessed 9/1/2010.
19. Vlatko Vedral, Decoding Reality, the Universe As Quantum Information, Oxford University Press, New York, 2010, p. 215.
20. Frank Close, 'Journey back to the beginning of time is nearly complete,' The Sunday Times, Times Newspapers Ltd 2011, 3 Thomas More Square, London E98 1XY, Registered in England No 894646, September 4, 2008. http://www.timesonline.co.uk/tol/news/science/article4670457.ece
21. Seth Lloyd, Programming The Universe, Vintage Books, Random House Inc. New York, New York 2007. ISBN: 978-1-4000-3386-7, p. 45.
22. Revelation 21:27, English Standard Version.
23. Genesis 1:1, English Standard Version.
24. Genesis 1:2, English Standard Version.
25. Frank J. Tipler, The Physics Of Christianity, Doubleday, New York, NY, 2007, ISBN 978-0-385-51424-8, p. 1.
26. Frank J. Tipler, The Physics Of Christianity, Doubleday, New York, NY, 2007, ISBN 978-0-26-51424-8, p. 1.
27. Gerald L. Schroeder, The Science of God, Free Press, New York, NY, 1997, ISBN 0-7679-0303-X, p. 56.
28. Genesis 1: 3, English Standard Version. 28. John 8:12, New King James Version.
29. John 8:12, English Standard Version.

30. SLAC National Accelerator Lab, Stanford University, web site accessed 11/4/2011. http://www2.slac.stanford.edu/vvc/theory/quarks.html
31. Mark Peplow, NATURE, Published online, 19 April 2005; doi:10.1038/ news050418-5, also see, Sam Jarman, Physics World, Quark–gluon plasma flows like water, calculations suggest, 09 Jun 2021, https://physicsworld.com/a/quark-gluon-plasma-flows-like-water-calculations-suggest/ accessed 10/3/2022.
32. Genesis 1:6-7, English Standard Version.
33. Isaiah 49:13, English Standard Version.
34. Alan Guth, Victor F. Weisskopf Professor of Physics MIT Department of Physics, Faculty, 2011 Massachusetts Institute of Technology http://web.mit.edu/physics/people/faculty/guth_alan.html
35. Jeremiah 51:15, English Standard Version.
Also, see Job 26:7, Isaiah 40:22, 42:5, 45:12, Jeremiah 10:12, Zechariah 12:1.
36. Mario Livio, The Accelerating Universe, John Wiley & Sons, Inc., 2000, New York, NY, ISBN 0-471-32969-X p. 54.
37. Mario Livio, Accelerating Universe, John Wiley & Sons, Inc., 2000, New York, NY, ISBN 0-471-32969-X p. 54
38. Genesis 1: 4-5, English Standard Version.
39. Mario Livio, The Accelerating Universe, John Wiley & Sons, Inc., 2000, New York, NY, ISBN 0-471-32969-X, p. 113.
40. Genesis 1:7, New King James Version.
41. Genesis 1:8, English Standard Version.
42. Genesis 1:9-10, English Standard Version.
43. Webmaster: Britt Griswold, NASA Official: Dr. Gary F. Hinshaw 'Five Year Results on the Oldest Light in the Universe,' WMAP 5-year Results Released – March 7, 2008. http://map.gsfc.nasa.gov/news/5yr_release.html
44. Charles Q. Choi, Space.com contributor, 'Discovery May Triple the Number of Stars In the Universe,' http://www.space.com/scienceastronomy/triple-amount-of-stars-...2 – posted: 01 December 2010, 01:03 pm ET. Also see, http://en.wikipedia.org/wiki/Dark_matter, Accessed 8/28/2010.
45. Stephen Hawking, Black Holes and Baby Universes and Other Essays, Bantam Books, New York, NY, 1993, ISBN 0-553-09523-4, p. 147.
46. Mario Livio, The Accelerating Universe, John Wiley & Sons, Inc., 2000, New York, NY, ISBN 0-471-32969-X p. 57

47. SPACE.com staff, Galaxies Protected by Dark Matter, posted: 12 March 2009, 09:16 am ET, accessed 8/28/2010. http://www.space.com/scienceastronomy/090312-hubble-dark-matter.html
48. Fraser Cain, Einstein's Cosmological Constant Predicts Dark Energy, Universe Today, University of Toronto, Canada, November 22, 2005. http://www.universetoday.com/11125/einsteins-cosmological-constant-predicts-dark-energy/
49. Mario Livio, The Accelerating Universe, John Wiley & Sons, Inc., 2000, New York, NY, ISBN 0-471-32969-X p. 163, 165, 166.
50. Robert Roy Britt, Senior Science Writer, 'Universe Measured: We're 156 Billion Light-years Wide!,' posted: 06:30 am ET 24 May 2004. http://www.space.com/scienceastronomy/mystery_monday_040524.html
51. Mario Livio, The Accelerating Universe, John Wiley & Sons, Inc., 2000, New York, NY, ISBN 0-471-32969-X, p. 171.
52. Luke 21:33, English Standard Version.
53. Psalm 102:25-26, New King James Version.
54. Mario Livio, The Accelerating Universe, John Wiley & Sons, Inc., 2000, New York, NY, ISBN 0-471-32969-X, p. 53.
55. Ann Spangler, Praying the Names of God, Zondervan, Grand Rapids Michigan 49530, 2004, ISBN 0-310-25353-5, p. 15.
56. 2 Peter 3:7, English Standard Version.
57. Gerald L. Schroeder, The Science of God, Free Press, New York, NY, 1997, ISBN 0-7679-0303-X p. p. 80.
58. Psalm 89:2, New King James Version.
59. Matthew 28:20, English Standard Version.
60. Revelation 21: 1, English Standard Version.
61. Isaiah 65:17, New King James Version.

Chapter 7: Substratum Of The Universe

1. Michelson, Albert Abraham & Morley, Edward Williams (1887). "On the Relative Motion of the Earth and the Luminiferous Ether". American Journal of Science 34: 333–345. http://en.wikipedia.org/wiki/Michelson-Morley_experiment#cite_note-michel2-2
2. Edwin F. Taylor and John Archibald Wheeler, 'Spacetime Physics: Introduction to Special Relativity, W. H. Freeman, 1992, ISBN 0-7167-2327-1. http://en.wikipedia.org/wiki/Special_relativity#cite_note-2

3. Albert Einstein, Relativity, 'The Special and The General Theory,' Translated by
Robert W. Lawson, Crown Publishers, Inc. New York, 1961, ISBN 0-517-029618, p. 30, 36, 37.
4. Resnick, Robert (1968). "Supplementary Topic B: The Twin Paradox". Introduction to Special Relativity. New York: John Wiley & Sons, Inc., p. 201. ISBN 0471717258. LCCN 67-031211. via August Kopff, Hyman Levy (translator), The Mathematical Theory of Relativity (London: Methuen & Co., Ltd., 1923), p. 52, as quoted by G. J. Whitrow, The Natural Philosophy of Time (New York: Harper Torchbooks, 1961), p. 215. http://en.wikipedia.org/wiki/Twin_paradox#cite_note-5
5. Brian Greene, The Fabric of the Cosmos: Space, Time, and the Texture of Reality,
First Vintage Books, Random House, New York, (Paperback) 2005, ISBN 0-375-72720-5, p. 49.
6. Isaiah 48:12, English Standard Version. 7. Exodus 3:14, English Standard Version.
8. Stephen Hawking, Black Holes and Baby Universes and Other Essays, Bantam Books, New York, NY, 1993, ISBN 0-553-09523-4, p. 9.
9. 1 John 1:5, English Standard Version.
10. John 4:24, English Standard Version.
11. Hebrews 4:12, New King James Version.
12. John 1:18, New King James Version.
13. Albert Einstein, Relativity, 'The Special and The General Theory,' Translated by
Robert W. Lawson, Crown Publishers, Inc. New York, 1961, ISBN 0-517-029618, p. 74, 75.
14. Jane S. Dietrich quoting Tony Redhead, The Caltech – Chile Connection, California Institute of Technology, Engineering and Science, Volume LXVII, Number 4, 2004, p. 9, 16.
15. Louisa Gilder, The Age Of Entanglement, When quantum Physics Was Reborn, Vintage Books, A Division of Random House, Inc., New York, 2008, ISBN 978-1-4000-9526-1, p. 102.
16. David Lindley, Uncertainty, Einstein, Heisenberg, Bohr, and the Struggle for the Soul of Science, Doubleday, New York, 2007, ISBN 978-0-385-51506-1, p.209
17. Richard Feynman, QED, The Strange Theory Of Light And Matter, Princeton University Press, Princeton NJ, 2006, ISBN 978-0-691-12575-6, p. 10.

18. J. Quagliano and L. Vallarino, Chemistry, Third Edition, Prentice-Hall, Inc., Englewood Cliffs, New Jersey, 1958, 1963, 1969, 69-10012, p. 219.
19. Dr. Christopher S. Baird, Why don't atoms collapse if they are mostly empty space?, published: January 12, 2013, https://wtamu.edu/~cbaird/sq/2013/01/12/why-dont-atoms-collapse-if-they-are-mostly-empty-space/, accessed 3/1/2021.
20. Kenneth Ford, 101 Quantum Questions, What You Need to Know about the World You Can't See, Harvard University Press, Cambridge Massachusetts, 2011, ISBN 978-0-674-05099- 0, p. 94.
21. Leon Lederman and Christopher Hill, Quantum Physics For Poets, Prometheus books, Amherst, New York, 2011, ISBN, 978-1-61614-233-9, p. 246, 247.
22. Kenneth Ford, 101 Quantum Questions, What You Need to Know about the World You Can't See, Harvard University Press, Cambridge Massachusetts, 2011, ISBN 978-0-674-05099- 0, p. 226, 227.
23. http://en.wikipedia.org/wiki/Niels_Bohr#cite_note-8 – Physics, accessed 8/9/2011. 24. Proverbs 8: 22-26, New King James Version.
25. Ann Spangler, Praying the Names of God, Zondervan, Grand Rapids Michigan 49530, 2004, ISBN 0-310-25353-5, p. 62.
26. Proverbs 3:19, New King James Version.

Chapter 8: Quantum Inscrutability

1. Laplace, translated by Pierre Simon, A Philosophical Essay on Probabilities, translated from the 6th French edition by Frederick Wilson Truscott and Frederick Lincoln Emory, Dover Publications, New York, 1951, p. 4. http://en.wikipedia.org/wiki/Pierre-Simon_Laplace
2. Heisenberg, Werner, 'Die Physik der Atomkerne,' Taylor & Francis, New York, New York, 1952, p. 30. http://en.wikipedia.or/wiki/Uncertainty_principle#cite_note-1
3. Stephen Hawking, A Brief History of Time, Bantam Books, New York, NY, 1988, ISBN 0-553- 05340-X, p. 77.
4. Nick Herbert, Quantum Reality, Beyond the New Physics, Anchor Press/ Doubleday, Garden City, New York, 1985, ISBN 0-385-18704-1, p. 119.
5. John 3:8, New King James Version.
6. Frank J. Tipler, The Physics Of Christianity, Doubleday, New York, NY, 2007, ISBN 978-0-385-51424-8, p. 264.

7. Gerald L. Schroeder, The Science of God, Free Press, New York, NY, 1997, ISBN 0-7679-0303-X, p. 171.
8. Ecclesiastes 9:11, New King James Version.
9. 2 Chronicles 18:33, New King James Version.
10. Luke 10:31, New King James Version.
11. Ephesians 1:4-5, English Standard Version.
12. Ephesians 2:10, English Standard Version.
13. Job 1:12, New King James Version.
14. 1 Kings 19:11-12, New King James Version.
15. Romans 8:28, New King James Version.
16. Luke 13:1-5, English Standard Version.
17. Deuteronomy 30:19, New King James Version.
18. Patrick S. Franklin, Perspectives on Science and Christian Faith, Volume 74, American Scientific Affiliation, Number 1, March 2022, p. 40, 42, 43.
19. John McArthur, Why Does God Allow So Much Suffering and Evil?, https://www.youtube.com/watch?v=6LFzk1afiD8, posted 2015, accessed June 14, 2023, minute 3:56, minute 35:33.
20. 1 Samual 2:6-8, Amos 3:6, Isaiah 45:5-7, New King James Version.
21. John McArthur, Why Does God Allow So Much Suffering and Evil?, https://www.youtube.com/watch?v=6LFzk1afiD8, posted 2015, accessed June 14, 2023, minute 27:18, minute 56:53.
22. Romans 3:5, New King James Version.
23. John McArthur, Why Does God Allow So Much Suffering and Evil?, https://www.youtube.com/watch?v=6LFzk1afiD8, posted 2015, accessed June 14, 2023, minute 45:10.
24. John McArthur, Why Does God Allow So Much Suffering and Evil?, https://www.youtube.com/watch?v=6LFzk1afiD8, posted 2015, accessed June 14, 2023, minute 55:19, 56:28, and Revelation 15:1-3, NKJV.
25. John McArthur, Why Does God Allow So Much Suffering and Evil?, https://www.youtube.com/watch?v=6LFzk1afiD8, posted 2015, accessed June 14, 2023, minute 1:03:00.
26. Werner Heisenberg, Physics and Philosophy, The Revolution In Modern Science, Harper Perennial, Modern Thought, New York, New York, 1958, 1962, ISBN 978-0-06-120919-2, p. 23.
27. Evan Harris Walker, The Physics of Consciousness, 2000, Perseus Publishing, Cambridge Massachusetts, ISBN 0-7382-0436-6, p. 87.
28. Werner Heisenberg, Physics and Philosophy, The Revolution In Modern Science, Harper Perennial, Modern Thought, New York, New

York, 1958, 1962, ISBN 978-0-06-120919-2, p. 28. http://en.wikipedia.org/wiki/Uncertainty_principle#cite_note-1, accessed May 2011.
29. Richard Feynman, QED, The Strange Theory Of Light and Matter, Princeton University Press, Princeton, New Jersey, 1985, ISBN 978-0-691-12575-6, p.41.
30. Don Eigler (of IBM moved 35 Xenon atoms), IBM spelled with 35 Xenon Atoms, Date added: 28 Sep 2009, accessed 8/10/2011. http://www-03.ibm.com/press/us/en/photo/28500.wss
31. Niels Bohr, The Philosophical Writings of Niels Bohr, Volume 1, Atomic Theory And The Description Of Nature, Ox Bow Press, Woodbridge, Connecticut, 1987 Reprint, first published 1934, Reprinted by permission of Cambridge University Press, ISBN 0-918024-50-1, p. 78, 68.
32. Werner Heisenberg, Physics and Philosophy, The Revolution In Modern Science, Harper Perennial, Modern Thought, New York, New York, 1958, 1962, ISBN 978-0-06-120919-2, p. 23.
33. Nick Herbert, Quantum Reality, Beyond the New Physics, Anchor Press/ Doubleday, Garden City, New York, 1985, ISBN 0-385-18704-1, p. 160.
34. Neils Bohr, (1920), "Über die Serienspektra der Element", Zeitschrift für Physik, p. 423– 478. See Stanford Encyclopedia of Philosophy, Bokulich, Alisa, "Bohr's Correspondence Principle", The Stanford Encyclopedia of Philosophy (Winter 2010 Edition), Edward N. Zalta (ed.) https://plato.stanford.edu/entries/bohr-correspondence/
35. Erwin Schrödinger, 'What is Life? With Mind and Matter and Autobiographical Sketches,' Cambridge University Press, New York, Nineteenth printing 2010,
ISBN 978-0-521-42708-1, p. 8 and 18.
36. Bernard Haisch, The God Theory, Universes, Zero-Point Fields, and What's Behind It All, Weiser Books, San Francisco, CA/ Newburyport, MA, 2009,
ISBN 978-1-57863-436-1, p. p. 72, 73 and 122.
37. Driscoll, J.T. (1911), Miracle, In The Catholic Encyclopedia, New York,
Robert Appleton Company. Retrieved August 10, 2011 from New Advent: http://www.newadvent.org/cathen/10338a.htm, Referenced St. Augustine, City of God XXI.8
38. Frank J. Tipler, The Physics Of Christianity, Doubleday, New York, NY, 2007, ISBN 978-0-385-51424-8, p. 200.

39. John 9:3 English Standard Version.
40. James 5:16, New King James Version.
41. Luke 3:14, English Standard Version.
42. John 17:15, New King James Version.
43. Romans 12:21, English Standard Version.
44. Psalm 31:24, New King James Version.
45. Luke 22:39-44, English Standard Version.
46. Romans 8:28, New King James Version.
47. John 15:13, King James Version.
48. Hebrews 12:2-3, King James Version.
49. Luke 10:20, New King James Version.

Chapter 9: A World Of Possibility

1. Manjit Kumar, Quantum, Einstein, Bohr, And The Great Debate About The Nature Of Reality, W. W. Norton & Company, New York, 2008, ISBN 978-0-393-07829-9p. 242, 243.
2. Bruce Rosenblum and Fred Kuttner, Quantum Enigma, Physics Encounters Consciousness, Oxford University Press, New York, New York, ISBN 978-0-19-517559-2, p. 67.
3. 2 Corinthians 4:8-10, English Standard Version. 4. Mark 8:35, English Standard Version.
5. David McMahon, Quantum Mechanics Demystified, McGraw Hill, New York, 2005, ISBN 0-07-145546-9, p. 13
6. Marcus Y. Woo, The Schrodinger Equation, Engineering & Science, California Institute of Technology, Volume LXXVI, Number 1, Spring 2013, page 9.
7. Jim Al-Khalili, Quantum, A Guide for the Perplexed, Weidenfeld & Nicolson, Orion House, London, 2003, ISBN 978-1-841-88238-3, p. 90, 91.
8. Andrew Whitaker, Einstein, Bohr and The Quantum Dilemma, Cambridge University Press, Cambridge, England, ISBN 0-521-48220-8, p. 145, 146.
9. Louisa Gilder, The Age Of Entanglement, When quantum Physics Was Reborn, Vintage Books, A Division of Random House, Inc., New York, 2008, ISBN 978-1-4000-9526-1, p. 65.
10. Evan Harris Walker, The Physics of Consciousness, Perseus Publishing, Cambridge Massachusetts, 2000, ISBN 0-7382-0436-6, p. 301.

11. Marcus Chown, The Quantum Zoo, A Tourist's Guide to the Neverending Universe, Joseph Henry Press, Washington, D.C., 2006, ISBN 0-309-09622-7, p. 31, 32.
12. Seth Lloyd, Programming The Universe, Vintage Books, Random House Inc. New York, New York 2007. ISBN: 978-1-4000-3386-7, p. 24.
13. Romans 7:18, New International Version.
14. Frank J. Tipler, The Physics Of Christianity, Doubleday, New York, NY, 2007, ISBN 978-0-385-51424-8, p. 260.
15. Paul Davies, God & The New Physics, Simon & Schuster, New York, 1983, ISBN 0-671-47688-2, p. 173.
16. Robert Spitzer, New Proofs For The Existence Of God, Contributions Of Contemporary Physics And Philosophy, William B. Eerdmans Publishing Company, Grand Rapids Michigan/ Cambridge, U.K., 2010, ISBN 978-0-8028-6383-6, p. 98-100.
17. Nick Herbert, Quantum Reality, Beyond the New Physics, Anchor Press/ Doubleday, Garden City, New York, 1985, ISBN 0-385-18704-1, p. 242.
18. Stephen Hawking and Leonard Mlodinow, The Grand Design, Bantam Books, New York, NY, 2010, ISBN 978-0-553-80537-6, p. 136.
19. Stephen Hawking and Leonard Mlodinow, The Grand Design, Bantam Books, New York, NY, 2010, ISBN 978-0-553-80537-6, p. 181.
20. Natalie Wolchover and Simons Science News, Supersymmetry Fails Test, Forcing Physics to Seek New Ideas, Simons Science News, Scientific American, Nature Publishing Group, New York, November 29, 2012. http://www.scientificamerican.com/article.cfm?id=supersymmetry-fails-test-forcing-physics- seek-new-idea – accessed 8/13/2013.
21. Frank J. Tipler, The Physics Of Christianity, Doubleday, New York, NY, 2007, ISBN 978-0-385-51424-8, p. 88.

Chapter 10: The Measure Of Reality

1. Proverbs 23:1, English Standard Version.
2. Deuteronomy 25:15, New International Version.
3. Werner Heisenberg, Physics and Philosophy, The Revolution In Modern Science, Harper Perennial, Modern Thought, New York, New York, 1958, 1962, ISBN 978-0-06-120919-2, p. 28.
4. Nick Herbert, Quantum Reality, Beyond the New Physics, Anchor Press/ Doubleday, Garden City, New York, 1985, ISBN 0-385-18704-1, p. 245.

5. Nick Herbert, Quantum Reality, Beyond the New Physics, Anchor Press/ Doubleday, Garden City, New York, 1985, ISBN 0-385-18704-1, p. 27.
6. Roger Penrose, The Large, the Small and the Human Mind, Cambridge University Press, Cambridge, UK, 1997, ISBN 0 521 78572 3 paperback, p. 3.
7. Evan Harris Walker, The Physics of Consciousness, Perseus Publishing, Cambridge Massachusetts, 2000, ISBN 0-7382-0436-6, p. 97.
8. Werner Heisenberg, Across The Frontiers, translated by Peter Heath, Ox Bow Press, Woodbridge, Connecticut, 1990 Reprint, ISBN 0-918024-80-3, P. 227.
9. Bruce Rosenblum and Fred Kuttner, Quantum Enigma, Physics Encounters Consciousness, Oxford University Press, New York, New York, ISBN 978-0-19-517559-2, p. 100.
10. Evan Harris Walker, The Physics of Consciousness, Perseus Publishing, Cambridge Massachusetts, 2000, ISBN 0-7382-0436-6, p. 138.
11. Werner Heisenberg, Physics and Philosophy, The Revolution In Modern Science, Harper Perennial, Modern Thought, New York, New York, 1958, 1962, ISBN 978-0-06-120919-2, p. 103.
12. Hideo Mabuchi, 'The Quantum- Classical Transition on Trial: Is the Whole More Than the Sum of the Parts?,' California Institute of Technology, Engineering and Science, Volume LXV, Number 2, 2002, p. 29.
13. Roger Penrose, The Large, the Small and the Human Mind, Cambridge University Press, Cambridge, UK, 1997, ISBN 0 521 78572 3 paperback. p. 175. Or 176.
14. Freeman Dyson, Progress In Religion, A talk by, his acceptance speech for the Templeton Prize, Washington National Cathedral, 9 May 2000. Also, Edge 68 — May 16, 2000, p. 6. http://www.edge.org/documents/archive/edge68.html
15. Fred Alan Wolf, Star Wave, Mind, Consciousness, and Quantum Physics, Macmillan Publishing Company, New York, 1984, ISBN 0-02-630860-6, p. 202.
16. Gerald L. Schroeder, The Science of God, Free Press, New York, NY, 1997, ISBN 0-7679-0303-X, p. 187.
17. Bruce Rosenblum and Fred Kuttner, Quantum Enigma, Physics Encounters Consciousness, Oxford University Press, New York, New York, ISBN 978-0-19-517559-2, p. 190.

18. Luke 19:40, English Standard Version.
19. Romans 8:22, New American Standard Bible.
20. Psalm 148:3, New King James Version.
21. Psalm 69:34, New King James Version.
22. D. A. Baylor, T. D. Lamb and K. W. Yau, Response Of Retinal Rods To Single Photons, Department of Neurobiology, Stanford, California12 June 1978, p.19.
23. Richard Feynman, QED, The Strange Theory Of Light And Matter, Princeton University Press, Princeton NJ, 2006, ISBN 978-0-691-12575-6, p. 24.
24. Brian Clegg, The God Effect: quantum entanglement, science's strangest phenomenon, St. Martin's Press, New York, N.Y., 2006, ISBN -13: 978-0-312-34341-5, p. 81
25. Manjit Kumar, Quantum, Einstein, Bohr, and the Great Debate About The Nature Of Reality, W. W. Norton & Company, New York, London, 2008, ISBN 978-0-393-07829-9, p. 54, 55.
26. Marcus Chown, The Quantum Zoo, A Tourist's Guide to the Neverending Universe, Joseph Henry Press, Washington, D.C., 2006, ISBN 0-309-09622-7, p. 33.
27. Gerald L. Schroeder, The Science of God, Free Press, New York, NY, 1997, ISBN 0-7679-0303-X, p. 156.
28. Seth Lloyd, Programming The Universe, Vintage Books, Random House Inc. New York, New York 2007. ISBN: 978-1-4000-3386-7, p. 107, 108.
29. Paul Davies, God & The New Physics, Simon & Schuster, New York, 1983, ISBN 0-671-47688-2, p. 111.
30. Niels Bohr. BrainyQuote.com, Xplore Inc, 2011. Web site accessed August 15, 2011. http://www.brainyquote.com/quotes/quotes/n/nielsbohr164546.html
31. Isaiah 40:12, New King James Version.
32. Ann Spangler, Praying the Names of God, Zondervan, Grand Rapids Michigan 49530, 2004, ISBN 0-310-25353-5, p. 27.
33. Carl Sagan, Cosmos, A Ballantine Book, Random House Publishing Group, New York, 1980, ISBN 0-345-33135-4, p. 212.
34. Mark 4:24, English Standard Version.
35. Matthew 9:29, English Standard Version.
36. Eric Metaxas, Letter To The American Church, Salem Books, Washington D.C., 2022, ISBN 978-1-68451-389-5 p. 112, 113.

37. Francis A. Schaeffer, Escape From Reason, Inter-Varsity Press, 1968, 130 North Wells, Chicago, Illinois 60606 Library of Congress Catalog Card Number 68-58084, p. 58.
38. Matthew 16:17, English Standard Version.

Chapter 11: Einstein's 'Spooky' Action At A Distance – The God Effect

1. Brian Clegg, The God Effect: quantum entanglement, science's strangest phenomenon, St. Martin's Press, New York, N.Y., 2006, ISBN -13: 978-0-312-34341-5, p. 2
2. Markus Aspelmeyer and Anton Zeilinger, A Quantum Renaissance, Physics World July 2008, Institute Of Physics Publishing Limited, Bristol, England, physicsworld.com, p. 24.
3. John Matson, Quantum Entanglement Links Two Diamonds, Scientific American, Nature Publishing Group, New York, December 1, 2011. http://www.scientificamerican.com/article.cfm?id=room-temperature-entanglement
4. Seth Lloyd, Programming The Universe, Vintage Books, Random House Inc. New York, New York 2007. ISBN: 978-1-4000-3386-7, p. 6.
5. Frank J. Tipler, The Physics Of Christianity, Doubleday, New York, NY, 2007, ISBN 978-0-385-51424-8, p. 49, 100.
6. Luke 12:7, English Standard Version.
7. Matthew 5:45, New King James Version.
8. Isaiah 55:9, English Standard Version.
9. Romans 3:12, English Standard Version.
10. John 1:1, Hebrews 4:15, and John 3:6, New King James Version.
11. John 1:3, Matthew 16:17, New King James Version.
12. The Scofield Study Bible, New King James Version, Oxford University Press, New York, 2002 Edition, Note on p. 1359.
13. Timothy Keller, The Reason for God, Belief in an Age of Skepticism, Riverhead Books, New York, 2008, ISBN 978-1-59448-349-3, p. 223.
14. John 5:39-40, New King James Version.
15. John 6:53-54, New King James Version.
16. John 6:28-29, English Standard Version.
17. John 14:15-16, English Standard Version.
18. John 15:4-5, English Standard Version.
19. 2 Peter 1:3-4, English Standard Version.
20. Corinthians 6:17, English Standard Version.

21. Ephesians 3:16, English Standard Version.
22. Romans 8:1, New King James Version.
23. 1 John 1:7, New King James Version.
24. Werner Heisenberg, Positivism, Metaphysics, and Religion, The Word Treasury of Physics, Astronomy, and Mathematics, edited by Timothy Ferris, Little, Brown and Company, Boston, 1991, ISBN 0-316-28133-6, p. 826.
25. Roger Penrose, The Road To Reality, A Complete Guide to The Laws of The Universe, Vintage Books, A Division of Random House, New York, 2004, ISBN 978-0679-77631-4, p. 591-593.
26. Vlatko Vedral, Decoding Reality, the Universe As Quantum Information, Oxford University Press, New York, 2010, p. 147, 148.
27. Michael Nielsen, Rules for a Complex Quantum World, an Exciting New Fundamental Discipline of Research Combines Information Science and Quantum Mechanics, Scientific American, October 15, 2002.
28. Lynn Yarris, Quantum Secrets of Photosynthesis Revealed, Research News, Berkley Lab, April 12, 2007, http://www.lbl.gov/Science-Articles/Archive/PBD-quantum-sec
29. Amit Goswami, Ph. D., The Self Aware Universe, How Consciousness Creates the Material World, Jeremy P. Thacher/ Putnam a member of Penguin Putnam Inc., New York, N. Y., 1995, ISBN 0-87477-798-4, p. 168.
30. Seth Lloyd, Programming The Universe, Vintage Books, Random House Inc. New York, New York 2007. ISBN: 978-1-4000-3386-7, p. 6, 138.
31. Ann Gibbon, D-Wave Press Release, D-Wave Systems sells its first Quantum Computing System to Lockheed Martin Corporation, Vancouver, B.C., May 25, 2011. Also see, M. W. Johnson, et al., Quantum annealing with manufactured spins, Nature, Nature 473, 194–198, (12 May 2011) doi:10.1038/ nature10012.
32. Jim Al-Khalili, Quantum, A Guide for the Perplexed, Weidenfeld & Nicolson, Orion House, London, 2003, ISBN 978-1-841-88238-3, p. 256, 257.
33. Vlatko Vedral, Entanglement Hits The Big Time, Nature (0028-0836), Volume 425, Issue 6953, Nature Publishing Group, Macmillan Publishers Limited, London, September 4, 2003, p. 192.
34. Seth Lloyd, Programming The Universe, Vintage Books, Random House Inc. New York, New York 2007. ISBN: 978-1-4000-3386-7, p. 57.
35. Seth Lloyd, Programming The Universe, Vintage Books, Random House Inc. New York, New York 2007. ISBN: 978-1-4000-3386-7, p. 16.

36. Michael Nielsen, Rules for a Complex Quantum World, an Exciting New Fundamental Discipline of Research Combines Information Science and Quantum Mechanics, Scientific American, October 15, 2002.
37. Seth Lloyd video, Seth Lloyd on the Universe as a Quantum Computer, https://www.youtube.com/watch?v=Qh8QfKVcvFA, accessed November 15, 2015.
38. Matthew 6:28-29, English Standard Version.

Chapter 12: Entanglement and Consciousness

1. Evan Harris Walker, The Physics of Consciousness, Perseus Publishing, Cambridge Massachusetts, 2000, ISBN 0-7382-0436-6, p. 151, 152.
2. Amit Goswami, The Self Aware Universe, How Consciousness Creates the Material World, Ph. D., Jeremy P. Thacher/ Putnam a member of Penguin Putnam Inc., New York, N. Y., 1995, ISBN 0-87477-798-4, p. 270.
3. Daniel C. Dennett, Consciousness Explained, Little, Brown and Company, New York, NY, 1991, ISBN 0-316-18065-3, p. 406.
4. Bruce Rosenblum and Fred Kuttner, Quantum Enigma, Physics Encounters Consciousness, Oxford University Press, New York, New York, ISBN 978-0-19-517559-2, p. 100.
5. Amit Goswami, The Self Aware Universe, How Consciousness Creates the Material World, Ph. D., Jeremy P. Thacher/ Putnam a member of Penguin Putnam Inc., New York, N. Y., 1995, ISBN 0-87477-798-4, p. 168.
6. Malcolm Longair, foreword for Roger Penrose, with Abner Shimony, Nancy Cartwright and Stephen Hawking, The Large, the Small and the Human Mind, Cambridge University Press, Cambridge, UK, 1997, ISBN 0 521 78572 3 paperback, edited by Malcom Longair, p. xvi.
7. Roger Penrose, The Large, the Small and the Human Mind, Cambridge University Press, Cambridge, UK, 1997, ISBN 0 521 78572 3 paperback, p. 116, 117.
8. Seth Lloyd, Programming The Universe, Vintage Books, Random House Inc. New York, New York 2007. ISBN: 978-1-4000-3386-7, p. 35.
9. Roger Penrose, The Large, The Small and the Human Mind, Cambridge University Press, 1997, 130-132.
10. Evan Harris Walker, The Physics of Consciousness, 2000, Perseus Publishing, Cambridge Massachusetts, ISBN 0-7382-0436-6, p. 237.

11. B. Katz and R. Milhei, 'The Effect of Temperature on the Synaptic Delay at the Neuromuscular Junction,' Journal of Physiology (London), 181, 1965, 656; quoted in Evan Harris Walker, The Physics of Consciousness, 2000, Perseus Publishing, Cambridge Massachusetts, ISBN 0-7382-0436-6, p. 225.
12. Gerald L. Schroeder, The Science of God, Free Press, New York, NY, 1997, ISBN 0-7679-0303-X, p. 33.
13. Anil Ananthaswamy, Consciousness Signature Discovered Spanning The Brain,
New Scientist, Reed Business Information Ltd, United Kingdom, 17 March 2009.
Journal reference: PLoS Biology, DOI: 10.1371/journal.pbio.1000061.
http://www.newscientist.com/article/dn16775-consciousness-signature-discovered-spanning- the-brain.html
Also, see Gerald L. Schroeder, The Hidden Face of God, Simon & Schuster, New York, NY, 2001, ISBN 0-684-87059-2, p. 155.
14. Roger Penrose, The Large, the Small and the Human Mind, Cambridge University Press, Cambridge, UK, 1997, ISBN 0 521 78572 3 paperback. p. 133.
15. Amit Goswami, Ph. D., The Self Aware Universe, How Consciousness Creates the Material World, Jeremy P. Thacher/ Putnam a member of Penguin Putnam Inc., New York, N. Y., 1995, ISBN 0-87477-798-4, p. 227.
16. Matthew 6:25-27, English Standard Version.
17. Evan Harris Walker, The Physics of Consciousness, 2000, Perseus Publishing, Cambridge Massachusetts, ISBN 0-7382-0436-6, p. 213.
18. Amit Goswami, The Self Aware Universe, How Consciousness Creates the Material World, Ph. D., Jeremy P. Thacher/ Putnam a member of Penguin Putnam Inc., New York, N. Y., 1995, ISBN 0-87477-798-4, p. 167.
19. Amit Goswami, Ph. D., The Self Aware Universe, How Consciousness Creates the Material World, Jeremy P. Thacher/ Putnam a member of Penguin Putnam Inc., New York, N. Y., 1995, ISBN 0-87477-798-4, p. 170.
20. C. S. Lewis, Mere Christianity, Harper, San Francisco, 1952, ISBN 0-06-065292-6, p. 21.
21. Evan Harris Walker, The Physics of Consciousness, 2000, Perseus Publishing, Cambridge Massachusetts, ISBN 0-7382-0436-6, p. 265.
22. Evan Harris Walker, The Physics of Consciousness, 2000, Perseus Publishing, Cambridge Massachusetts, ISBN 0-7382-0436-6, p. 237.

23. Evan Harris Walker, The Physics of Consciousness, 2000, Perseus Publishing, Cambridge Massachusetts, ISBN 0-7382-0436-6, p. 265.
24. Lee Smolin, Three Roads to Quantum Gravity, 2001, Basic Books, First published in Great Britain 2000 by Weidenfeld and Nicolson. ISBN 0-465-07836-2, p. 48.
25. John Preskill, Full Circle Physics, Engineering and Science, Caltech, Volume LXXVII, Number 3, Fall 2015, page 15.
26. Genesis 11:6, English Standard Version.
27. Nick Herbert, Quantum Reality, Beyond the New Physics, Anchor Press/ Doubleday, Garden City, New York, 1985, ISBN 0-385-18704-1, p. 249.
28. Genesis 2:24, English Standard Version.
29. Evan Harris Walker, The Physics of Consciousness, 2000, Perseus Publishing, Cambridge Massachusetts, ISBN 0-7382-0436-6, p. 330.
30. Evan Harris Walker, The Physics of Consciousness, 2000, Perseus Publishing, Cambridge Massachusetts, ISBN 0-7382-0436-6, p. 330.
31. Vlatko Vedral, Entanglement Hits The Big Time, Nature (0028-0836), Volume 425, Issue 6953, Nature Publishing Group, Macmillan Publishers Limited, London, September 4, 2003, p. 28, 29.
32. Johnjoe McFadden, Quantum Evolution, How Physics' Weirdest Theory Explains Life's Biggest Mystery, W.W. Norton & Company, New York, ISBN 0-393-05041-6, p. 237, 315.
33. Niels Bohr, The Philosophical Writings of Niels Bohr, Volume 1, Atomic Theory And The Description Of Nature, Ox Bow Press, Woodbridge, Connecticut, 1987 Reprint, first published 1934, Reprinted by permission of Cambridge University Press, ISBN 0-918024-50-1, p. 119.
34. Gilbert Ryle, The Concept of Mind, University of Chicago Press, Chicago, ISBN 0-226-73296-7, 1949, p. 27, 155.
35. Mark 12:27, New King James Version.
36. John Lenox, Why Science and Atheism Don't Mix, July 17, 2020, 7:02 AM, accessed September 11, 2020. https://evolutionnews.org/2020/07/why-science-and-atheism-dont-mix/

CHAPTER 13: Christ's Mission And Teleportation

1. Malcolm Ritter, Science fact: Scientists achieve 'Star Trek'-like feat, Associated Press, Copyright 1997, reported by CNN SCI-TECH Story

Page, December 10, 1997
Web posted at: 9:29 p.m. EST (0229 GMT). http://www.quantum.at/fileadmin/links/CNN/CNN.html
Also see, Mark Prigg, Beam me up: Scientists say human teleportation is 'possible' as they transfer atoms three metres in groundbreaking experiment, DailyMail.com, 29 May 2014, accessed Nov 26th 2015. http://www.dailymail.co.uk/sciencetech/article-2643332/Beam-Scientists-sat-teleportation- possible-transfer -atoms.html
2. Mark Prigg, Beam me up: Scientists say human teleportation is 'possible' as they transfer atoms three metres in groundbreaking experiment, Mail Online, Published: 18:42 EDT, 29 May 2014 | Updated: 02:08 EDT, 30 May 2014. Accessed November 25, 2015. https://www.dailymail.co.uk/sciencetech/article-2643332/Beam-Scientists-sat-teleportation-possible-transfer-atoms.html
3. Genesis 5:24, New King James Version.
4. John 20:19, English Standard Version.
5. Acts 5:22-23, New King James Version.
6. Acts 8: 38-40, New King James Version.
7. Anton Zeilinger, Harnessing Quanta, Quantum Teleportation, Scientific American, Nature Publishing Group, New York, Updated from the April 2000 Issue, p. 37-40. www sciam.com
8. Anton Zeilinger, Dance of the Photons: From Einstein to Quantum Teleportation, Farrar, Straus and Giroux, New York, N.Y., 2010, ISBN 978-0-374-23966-4, p. 52-53.
Also see, Brian Clegg, The God Effect: quantum entanglement, science's strangest phenomenon, St. Martin's Press, New York, N.Y., 2006, ISBN -13: 978-0-312-34341-5, p. 209, 210.
9. Louisa Gilder, The Age Of Entanglement, When quantum Physics Was Reborn, Vintage Books, A Division of Random House, Inc., New York, 2008, ISBN 978-1-4000-9526-1, p. 317.
10. 2 Corinthians 5:21, New King James Version.
11. Revelation 1:5, New King James Version.
12. Isaiah 53: 4-5, English Standard Version.
13. Hebrews 4:15, New King James Version.
14. Matthew 26:39, New King James Version.
15. Hebrews 2:17, English Standard Version.
16. Isaiah 46:9-10, New King James Version.
17. Frank J. Tipler, The Physics Of Christianity, Doubleday, New York, NY, 2007, ISBN 978-0- 385-51424-8, p. 100.
18. Revelation 13:8, New King James Version.

19. Hebrews 9:28 New King James Version.
20. Hebrews 2:8, New American Standard Bible.
21. Hebrews 11:1, New King James Version.
22. John 6:54, New King James Version.
23. John 3:6, New King James Version.
24. John 14:6, English Standard Version.
25. John 1:1-4, New King James Version.
26. 1 Corinthians 13:12, New King James Version.
27. Isaiah 55:6, New King James Version.
28. Matthew 7:19-20, New King James Version.
29. John 10:27-29, New King James Version.
30. Revelation 3:5, New International Version.
31. John 6:63 English Standard Version.
32. Mark 4:3-8, English Standard Version.
33. 2 Corinthians 5:17, English Standard Version.
34. Matthew 7:19-20, New King James Version.
35. James 2:20, New King James Version.
36. John 3:7, English Standard Version.
37. Genesis 22:12, New King James Version.
38. Job 1:1, New King James Version.
39. Job 9:33, New King James Version.
40. Job 13:15, New King James Version.
41. Job 19:25-27, New King James Version.
42. Romans 12:5, New King James Version.
43. John 13:34-35, New King James Version.
44. 2 Corinthians 5:17, New King James Version.
45. 1 Corinthians 15:52, New King James Version.
46. 1 Corinthians 15: 20, New King James Version.
47. 1 Corinthians 15: 14, New King James Version.
48. Luke 24:11, 25-43, Mark 16:9-11, John 20:26-28, John 21:1-14.
49. 1 Corinthians 15:6, English Standard Version.
50. Acts 2:1-4, 3:14, English Standard Version.
51. Josh McDowell, Evidence that Demands a Verdict, Campus Crusade for Christ International, Arrowhead Springs, San Bernardino, CA 92414, page 45, 46 and pages 185-273.
52. Matthew 27:62-66, English Standard Version.
53. Josh McDowell, Evidence that Demands a Verdict, Campus Crusade for Christ International, Arrowhead Springs, San Bernardino, CA 92414, pages 174 -184.
54. John 6:40, English Standard Version.

55. Romans 10:9, English Standard Version
56. John 4:19, New King James Version.
57. Romans 8:32, New King James Version.
58. John 1:18, Good News Translation.
59. John 16:3, 33, New King James Version.

Eigen Publishing

Orange County, California

Made in the USA
Columbia, SC
12 July 2024

38534575R00143